Contents

Introduction

RECEPTIVE SKILLS
Reading

There are ten tests in reading comprehension. They test the reading strategies practised in the corresponding modules in the Students' Book:
* prediction
* multiple choice
* finding facts and opinions

The tasks in the tests include:
* true/false
* multiple choice questions
* multiple matching

In each test the students may score up to 10 points. One point is given for the correct answer.

The answer key to the reading comprehension tests is provided at the back of this Test Book.

Listening

There are ten tests in listening comprehension. They test the listening strategies practised in the corresponding modules in the Students' Book:
* prediction
* listening for gist
* listening for specific information

The listening tests include:
* true/false
* multiple choice questions
* multiple matching

In each test the students may score up to 10 points. One point is given for the correct answer. The students should listen to each recording twice.

The tapescripts and the answer key to the listening comprehension tests are provided at the back of this Test Book.

PRODUCTIVE SKILLS
Speaking

There are ten tests in speaking. The paired format (two students and a teacher) of the speaking tests aims to offer students the opportunity to demonstrate, in a controlled but friendly atmosphere, their ability to use their spoken language skills effectively. The collaborative tasks make it possible for the teacher to elicit an adequate sample of their students' best language and to provide an accurate and fair assessment of it. Therefore, students should be able to provide full but natural answers to the questions and to speak clearly and audibly at all times. They should not be afraid to ask for clarification if they have not understood what has been said.

The approximate time of each test is 10–15 minutes as some tests require some student preparation (3–4 minutes), e.g. Test 5, Test C, Test 7, Final Test.

The format allows the teacher to assess listening to the students' conversations and information exchanges. Alternatively, the teacher could act as interlocutor and manage the interaction either by asking questions or providing cues for the students. It is the teacher's role to ensure that both students are given an equal opportunity to speak.

The role of the students is to maintain the interaction as much as possible and take equal turns in the information exchange so as to provide the teacher/examiner with an adequate amount of language to assess.

The tasks are varied and they always refer to the leading theme of each Module in the Students' Book. They focus on:
* exchanging personal information
* exchanging factual information
* expressing opinions
* planning and decision making
* reaching a consensus
* negotiating
* describing pictures
* giving a short presentation

Students are assessed on their performance throughout the whole test according to the following criteria:

1 Accuracy
   • correctness of grammar structures
   • use of grammar structures
   • accurate use of syntactic forms
   • right choice of vocabulary
   • pronunciation (sounds, word stress, intonation patterns)

2 Fluency
   • pace of speech
   • use of fillers and hesitation
   • number of pauses
   • 'playing for time'
   • linking devices

3 Interaction and collaboration
   • turn-taking
   • initiating and responding
   • maintaining conversation
   • reasonable use of time provided

4 Task achievement/appropriacy
   • getting the message across
   • use of prompts provided
   • ability to express ideas in a coherent way
   • ability to justify opinions
   • completion of the task (reaching a conclusion, an agreement, etc.)
   • relevance of language to the task

In each task, students may get a total of 20 points.
• accuracy   1–5 points
• fluency   1–5 points
• interaction and collaboration   1–5 points
• task achievement and appropriacy   1–5 points

Writing

There are ten tests in writing. They all relate closely to the topics in the Students' Book Modules and are based on the Writing Helps at the back of the Students' Book. The writing tests aim to offer students the opportunity to demonstrate their ability to use their written language skills effectively.

The following writing task types are covered:
• a notice
• an email advert
• an advert to sell something
• an email of invitation
• description of a sport
• a formal letter
• an Internet page
• a letter of complaint
• description of a place
• a report

Each test has a total of 20 points. The criteria for assessment include:
• range of vocabulary and structures
  used   1–5 points
• organisation, linking and register   1–5 points
• coverage of points and presentation
  of ideas   1–5 points
• relevance to topic, handwriting,
  spelling   1–5 points

Test 1 A USE OF ENGLISH

A Put the verbs in brackets into the Present Simple or the Present Continuous. (5 points)

0 She ___likes___ (like) cooking very much.

1 He can't talk to you right now. He _____ (have) a bath.

2 I usually _____ (have) lunch at about 2 o'clock.

3 Her parents _____ (not believe) in God.

4 Tom is a well-known author but he _____ (not write) anything at the moment.

5 They don't want to help me now. They _____ (watch) TV.

B Use verbs from the box in the Present Perfect to complete the sentences. (4 points)

> drink, win, feed, not clean, lose

0 They are very happy about the lottery.

They ___have won a lot of money___ .

1 There is no more juice left. Someone _____

_____ .

2 The bathroom is still dirty. We _____

_____ .

3 She can't find her passport. I'm afraid she _____

_____ .

4 The cats are not hungry any more. I _____

_____ .

C Use the prepositions from the box to complete the text. (2 points)

> for, from, at, of, in

My brother Tom is very different (0) ___from___ me. He loves learning mathematics and physics and I am very bad (1) _____ them. I prefer studying English and French because I think languages are necessary (2) _____ travelling. They are also useful (3) _____ communicating on the Internet. My brother doesn't study any foreign language because he says he is tired (4) _____ learning new words and grammar.

D Write the words from the box under the correct verbs. (3 points)

> the housework, plans, a noise, jogging, a lot of exercise, the beds

GO:

_____

DO:

_____

MAKE:

_____

E Complete the sentences with the appropriate words. The first letter of each word is given. (6 points)

1 Somebody who is satisfied or happy about something is p_____ .

2 A house with only one storey is called a b_____ .

3 Before we have a meal my children always help me and I_____ the table.

4 I keep all my clothes in this w_____ .

5 I'm sorry to hear that you didn't p_____ your driving test.

6 A person who is unhappy and thinks about problems all the time is w_____ .

Total | 20

Test 1 B USE OF ENGLISH

A Put the verbs in brackets into the Present Simple or the Present Continuous. (5 points)

0 She _____likes_____ (like) cooking very much.

1 Let's go to the cinema! They _____ (show) a good film at The Odeon.

2 I'm afraid she _____ (not love) you any more.

3 Joanna, this is Mike, my friend from work. We _____ (work) on a new project together.

4 My mother _____ (think) that I am too young to go on this trip on my own.

5 I _____ (study) maths now but in the future I would like to be a TV presenter.

B Use verbs from the box in the Present Perfect to complete the sentences. (4 points)

eat, win, not paint, break, spend

0 They are very happy about the lottery.

They _have won a lot of money_____ .

1 The video doesn't work. I think my little brother

_____ .

2 I don't have any money on me. I'm afraid I _____

_____ .

3 There is no more chicken left. Someone _____

_____ .

4 The walls of the kitchen look dirty. We _____

_____ .

C Use the prepositions from the box to complete the text. (2 points)

with, from, at, of, in

My sister Stephanie is very different (0) _____from_____ me. She is interested (1) _____ zoology and enjoys working with animals. I must say she is very good (2) _____ it. I hate animals and I am afraid (3) _____ big dogs and all insects. Biology is much more interesting for me. But Steph is bored (4) _____ learning about trees and flowers.

D Write the words from the box under the correct verbs. (3 points)

a mistake, repairs, a shower, a phone call, the cooking, an argument

MAKE:

_____

HAVE:

_____

DO:

_____

E Complete the sentences with the appropriate words. The first letter of each word is given. (6 points)

1 Somebody who has or uses original ideas is c_____ .

2 A s_____ house is one of the pair of houses joined together by a wall.

3 My children always help me with the housework: they make the beds and t_____ their rooms.

4 An electric machine for washing plates, cups and forks is called a d_____ .

5 His grandparents g_____ a lot of plants in their garden.

6 If you are a_____ with somebody you don't like what this person does or says.

Total	20

Test 1 LISTENING

Listen to the radio commercial, read the questions and circle the correct answer, a, b or c.

1 Hatton Hotels are located
  a in city centres.
  b close to city centres.
  c far from cities.

2 There are _____ Hatton Hotels all over the country.
  a less than forty hotels
  b forty hotels
  c more than forty hotels

3 Hatton Restaurants do not serve
  a fish dishes.
  b meat and salads.
  c light meals.

4 In every room in Hatton Hotels there is
  a a fridge.
  b a direct-line telephone.
  c a teapot and tea cups.

5 Every Hatton Cocktail Bar serves
  a classic steaks.
  b drinks.
  c vegetarian dishes.

6 The weekend tour of the area takes
  a two hours.
  b three hours.
  c four hours.

7 On departure day every hotel guest gets
  a an invitation for a special weekend tour.
  b a souvenir.
  c a free ticket to one of the local attractions.

8 The Hatton Hotel free phone number is
  a 0 800 768 563.
  b 0 800 786 563.
  c 0 800 768 536.

Total   **8**

Test 1 SPEAKING

Talk to your partner and exchange information about your personal lives.

Student A
Find out about your partner's life and ask questions about the following things:

- his/her hobbies;
- his/her favourite TV programme and TV star;
- his/her best friend from school;
- what he/she does at the weekend;
- what he/she is doing at the moment;
- what activities he/she finds stressful.

Total   **20**

Student B
Find out about your partner's life and ask questions about the following things:

- his/her likes and dislikes;
- his/her favourite music and pop star;
- his/her brother/sister;
- what he/she usually does after school;
- where he/she goes on holiday and what he/she does there;
- what activities he/she finds relaxing.

Total   **20**

Test 2 A Use of English

A Circle the correct alternative in each sentence.

(5 points)

0 My aunt lives in London, south of *Thames*/
the Thames.

1 He saw an accident when he *was driving/drove*
home.

2 I haven't done my homework *yet/already*.

3 I need to have *a bath/the bath* first.

4 I *didn't see/haven't seen* my friend recently.

5 When my mother heard the news she
was beginning/began to cry.

6 I *played/have played* computer games a lot
when I was a child.

7 I prefer travelling by *the train/train*, it's very
comfortable.

8 How many times *has he won/did he win* the
ski-jumping tournament this season?

9 Would you like to go to *a theatre/the theatre*
tonight?

10 What *did your sister do/was your sister doing*
when she finally got home yesterday?

B Read the text and put the verbs in brackets into the Past Simple, the Past Continuous or the Present Perfect.

(7 points)

I (0) ____met____ (meet) Carmela two years ago

when I (1) _____ (be) in Madrid on

a business trip. I (2) _____ (sit) in a café

with some business partners when a beautiful young

waitress (3) _____ (come up) to us to take

the order. I (4) _____ (speak) to her in my

broken Spanish and we (5) _____ (fall) in

love with each other at first sight. The next day we

(6) _____ (have) our first date. This year she

(7) _____ (visit) me in Poland twice.

C Complete the sentences with the correct form of the word in brackets.

(4 points)

0 There are more and more ___homeless___ (home)
people in India.

1 My new job gives me financial _____
(independent) from my parents.

2 She is a very good tennis player and can teach you
how to _____ (success) in playing tennis.

3 After the accident my leg was so _____
(pain) that I couldn't walk.

4 I think Sara is not a good journalist because of her
_____ (able) to listen to other people.

5 My children are so _____ (decision) about
their holidays – one day they want to go to the
mountains, the next day they prefer the seaside.

6 I'm very sorry to hear that your grandfather is
_____ (die).

7 My teacher's _____ (angry) was so great
that I was afraid of talking to him.

8 Tom's mother became _____ (suspect) when
he returned home after midnight.

D Choose the adjectives from the box to complete the sentences. There are more adjectives than you need.

(4 points)

skilful, ~~busy~~, boring, proud, overrated, wise, cruel, generous,
sensitive, kind, ambitious, calm

0 A ___busy___ person has many things to do
all the time.

1 Something uninteresting is _____ .

2 Don't criticise him, he will start crying. Don't you
know he is very _____ ?

3 My aunt is a very _____ person. She
always gives money to charities and helps the poor.

4 When we saw a python everybody panicked except
John. He stayed _____ .

5 My little brother is very _____ to animals.
He always kicks and hits them.

6 I'm afraid their new record is _____ . It is
not as good as everybody says.

7 My boyfriend is very _____ . He always
helps me carry heavy bags.

8 The Impressionists were very _____ at
drawing and painting landscapes.

Total	20

Test 2 B USE OF ENGLISH

A Circle the correct alternative in each sentence.

(5 points)

0 My aunt lives in London, south of *Thames/* *the Thames.*

1 They *won/have won* three table-tennis tournaments when they were at school.

2 Fiona is very talented. She plays *the piano/piano* very well.

3 How many times *have you travelled/did you travel* by plane?

4 I don't like going to *cinema/the cinema*.

5 What *did you do/were you doing* when you got to school yesterday?

6 *The German/German* is a very difficult language to learn.

7 He *was reading/read* a newspaper when he heard a strange noise.

8 Have you visited our grandparents *yet/already*?

9 I *didn't ride/haven't ridden* a horse much this summer.

10 When they told him everything he *was calling/* *called* the police.

B Read the text and put the verbs in brackets into the Past Simple, the Past Continuous or the Present Perfect.

(7 points)

The first time I (0) _____saw_____ (see) Tom was on the first day of my secondary school. He (1) _____ (talk) to some friends and I (2) _____ (read) a book in our school hall. When I (3) _____ (hear) his voice I (4) _____ (like) it very much. Two months later we (5) _____ (begin) going out with each other. After finishing school Tom (6) _____ (go) to Canada to study law. This year he (7) _____ (come back) home for the Christmas holidays.

C Complete the sentences with the correct form of the word in brackets.

(4 points)

0 There are more and more _____homeless_____ (home) people in India.

1 Many people say that children have too much _____ (free) these days.

2 Be careful! There are a lot of _____ (poison) snakes in this forest.

3 At first they loved each other very much but later their love changed into _____ (hate).

4 The Smiths didn't want to do business with him when they learnt that he was very _____ (honest).

5 I didn't like classes in the morning but I loved evening _____ (active).

6 My grandmother died many years ago but my grandfather is still _____ (live).

7 This extra money will _____ (able) him to travel to Canada and the States.

8 John's first marriage was _____ (success), so he got divorced and married again.

D Choose the adjectives from the box to complete the sentences. There are more adjectives than you need.

(4 points)

generous, busy, brilliant, evil, hard-working, weak, arrogant, awful, violent, brave, wise, decisive

0 A _____busy_____ person has many things to do all the time.

1 I hate wars, blood and shooting. I never watch _____ films on TV.

2 Audrey is an absolutely _____ young actress. She will be a star in the future.

3 Are you still thinking about where to go on your holidays? Oh, come on! Be _____ !

4 My little son was really _____ and didn't cry at the dentist.

5 The film was just _____ ! I didn't like anything about it.

6 The Browns are _____ people – they spend ten hours in the office every day.

7 I always ask my grandfather for advice, he is a very _____ man.

8 Don't be so _____ ! You are not better or more important than other people.

Total | **20**

Test 2 READING

Read the text and decide if the statements are true (T) or false (F).

1 ☐ The story of Robin Hood has been known for 600 years.

2 ☐ William Tell, El Cid and Janosik are international heroes.

3 ☐ A sixteenth-century *History of Great Britain* includes a story about Robin Hood.

4 ☐ Robin Hood was King Edward II's knight.

5 ☐ It is probable that Robin Hood lived in the twelfth century.

6 ☐ There is a castle in the middle of Sherwood forest.

7 ☐ In the visitors' centre you can't watch a video about Robin's adventures.

8 ☐ According to tradition, Lady Marion became Robin Hood's wife in Edwinstowe church.

Robin Hood

The story of Robin Hood, the most popular English folk hero of all times, has reached every corner of the Earth. There are many versions of this well-known tale which is about 600 years old. Everybody knows Robin's friends (Little John, Brother Tuck, Will Scarlet), and the famous Sherwood Forest – Robin Hood's home and the place where many of his adventures took place. In other countries there are similar stories, such as William Tell in Switzerland, El Cid in Spain or Janosik in Poland, but only Robin Hood has become an 'international' hero.

Unfortunately, there is almost no evidence that Robin Hood really existed. Thirteenth-century ballads, fourteenth-century chronicles, a sixteenth-century *History of Great Britain*, all talk about Robin Hood. However, none of them tells us about the sources they used. In the 1800s and 1900s, historians found two Robin Hoods who lived in the fourteenth century. One of them was even King Edward II's servant. Later on, other historians found several different Hoods living in different parts of England – Robin was a popular Christian name and Hood was a fairly common surname. It seems that by 1337, the story of Robin Hood was well established. Most probably, he lived around the year 1200.

Today, the legend of Robin Hood has turned Nottinghamshire into a large tourist attraction. In the centre of Nottingham there is Nottingham Castle. Parts of it still recall the time of Robin Hood. Sherwood forest has an excellent visitor's centre with an attractive display and shop, and some very pleasant walks in the nearby forest. Edwinstowe church, in which, according to tradition, Robin Hood and Lady Marion were married, is one of the visitors' favourite sites.

Total ☐ 8

Test 2 WRITING

You have found a pair of eye glasses in the school cafeteria. Write a notice and:

- describe the eye glasses (colour, shape);
- say where and when you found them;
- give your contact details.

Total ☐ 20

Test A LISTENING

Listen to the story of Mickey Mouse and decide if the statements are true (T) or false (F).

1 ☐ Gertie the Dinosaur was the first cartoon character in cinema history.

2 ☐ Walt Disney gave Mickey Mouse his own voice.

3 ☐ Walt Disney drew Mickey Mouse himself.

4 ☐ Walt Disney produced his first black and white Mickey Mouse film in 1928.

5 ☐ Four famous characters joined Mickey in his films.

6 ☐ Children didn't like Mickey Mouse at first.

Total ☐ 6

Test A SPEAKING

Work in pairs. Student A reads Text A and Student B reads Text B. Ask questions about the missing information about Leonardo DiCaprio. Then answer the following questions together:

Do you like Leonardo DiCaprio?
Do you think he is a good actor?
What other actors and actresses do you like?
Why do you think they are good?
What roles do they play?

Text A
His full name is Leonardo Wilhelm DiCaprio. He was born on November 11, _____ in Los Angeles, California. It's no secret that Leo's one true love is _____ . Her name is Irmelin (she's _____) and she raised him on her own since he was a year old.

He is a famous actor himself and he has starred in _____ films since 1993 but he admires other actors, especially Robert DeNiro, Jack Nicholson and Meg Ryan. Leo likes reading and his favourite book is '*The Old Man and the Sea*' by Ernest Hemingway. He loves _____ and he is keen on Pink Floyd, The Beatles and Led Zeppelin. Leo's favourite colours are _____ and he is fond of basketball and baseball. He enjoys spending free time with _____ .

Total ☐ 20

Text B
His full name is Leonardo Wilhelm DiCaprio. He was born on November 11, 1974 in _____ , California. It's no secret that Leo's one true love is his mother. Her name is _____ (she's German) and she raised him on her own since he was a year old.

He is a famous actor himself and he has starred in nine films since _____ but he admires other actors, especially _____ Leo likes reading and his favourite book is _____ by Ernest Hemingway. He loves pasta and lemonade and he is keen on _____ . Leo's favourite colours are black and purple and he is fond of _____ He enjoys spending free time with his friends.

Total ☐ 20

Test A READING

Read the description of the lifestyle of the Amish people. Then match the paragraph titles (A–G) with the paragraphs (1–6). There is one extra title.

The Amish

1 _____ The name 'Amish' comes from Jacob Amman, a seventeenth-century bishop in Switzerland. Although the Amish originated in Europe, they emigrated to the USA in search of religious freedom.

2 _____ They live in small towns, also called settlements in nineteen states in the USA, southern Canada and Central America. No matter where they settled, they continued their traditional farm life and their religious customs.

3 _____ Amish children are frequently educated at home or in traditional Amish one-room schools and they do not attend classes after the eighth grade. The Amish teach their young people how to be homemakers and farmers, carpenters and tradesmen from a very early age.

4 _____ Some people think that the Amish are strange because they do not use petrol or electricity which pollute the environment. They are against cars, tractors, radio, television and telephones. They believe they should keep our planet clean.

5 _____ Choosing a wife or husband is the key decision in an Amish person's life. It is interesting that instead of a diamond or gold ring, a man gives his bride china or a clock before they get married. At the wedding ceremony, the bride wears a blue dress which is the most popular colour choice. Finally, the wedding usually takes place in November or December, on a Tuesday or Thursday. It is a fascinating event.

6 _____ They speak a dialect of German at home; they use 'standard' German at their church services; and they learn English at school. They speak English when they have to communicate with anyone who is not Amish.

A GETTING MARRIED
B LANGUAGES
C REASON TO EMIGRATE
D EDUCATION AND LEARNING
E HOPES FOR THE FUTURE
F ECOLOGY
G HOME TOWNS

Total	6

Test A WRITING

You want to join a pen friend site on the Internet. Write an email advert for a pen friend, and:

- briefly describe how you look and what kind of person you are;
- write about your interests;
- explain why you want to exchange letters in English.

Total	20

Test 3 A USE OF ENGLISH

A Use the expressions from the box to complete the sentences. Some are used more than once.

(4 points)

> must, mustn't, have to, don't have to, can, can't

0 You *don't have to* hurry. I'm sure they'll wait for you.

1 You _____ park here. Can't you see the sign? Parking is forbidden.

2 Tell them they _____ wash the carrots. I've already done it.

3 I _____ help you. I'm not busy now and I think I know how to repair your car.

4 Don't argue with me, son! You _____ do it right now!

5 I'm sorry, I _____ talk to you right now. I'm in a hurry.

6 Listen to me, boys! You _____ touch it, it's very hot!

7 The rules in our school are very strict. We _____ study hard and always be on time for our lessons.

8 You _____ have a visa to go to Germany. You need only a passport.

B Complete the text with the adjectives given in brackets in the correct form.

(5 points)

I have a lot of friends and three of them are even

(0) *closer* (close) to me than my brothers. Tom

is a very good student, certainly (1)_____

(good) than all the other boys in my class. He also

plays basketball very well because he is (2)_____

(tall) boy in our school team. Mark doesn't do any

sports at all but I like him because he is

(3)_____ (intelligent) person I know. He can

tell you a lot about insects and other animals. He is not

so good at numbers because for him maths is just

(4)_____ (interesting) than zoology. George,

my third friend, is (5)_____ (bad) pupil in our

school. He fails all tests and exams and our teacher

says he is (6)_____ (lazy) student she has ever

had. But I think George is (7)_____ (clever)

than my other classmates, he just doesn't have time to

study. He helps his mother a lot with the housework

and takes care of his two (8)_____ (young)

sisters. He is also (9)_____ (kind) of all my

friends. I think life is much (10)_____ (easy)

if you have some good friends around.

C Complete the sentences with the adjectives in brackets in the correct order.

(2 points)

0 She wants a (black, small) *small black* handbag for her birthday.

1 I bought a pair of (leather, Italian, fashionable) _____ shoes.

2 His new-born sister has got (dark brown, short, beautiful) _____ hair.

3 Who did you get these (bright red, horrible, wollen) _____

socks from?

4 I thought the film was boring but John liked the (British, young) _____ actress very much.

D Match the words from the two columns to form words that go together.

(4 points)

0 salty	a) clothes
1 public	b) meat
2 sit-down	c) meal
3 casual	d) crisps
4 mild	e) food
5 tinned	f) transport
6 advanced	g) technology
7 broken	h) cheese
8 tough	i) leg

0	1	2	3	4	5	6	7	8
d								

E Complete the sentences with the appropriate words. Use only <u>one</u> word in each gap.

(5 points)

0 I hate making *speeches* . I am just afraid of speaking in public.

1 Darling, you need to _____ on a sweater. It's getting cold.

2 Last year we went on a school _____ to Paris. It was great!

3 Let's get _____ for lunch one day next week, what do you think?

4 A woman on her wedding-day or just before it is called a _____ .

5 All football fans were very happy because it was the first _____ of our team in the World Cup.

Total	20

Test 3 B Use of English

A Use the expressions from the box to complete the sentences. Some are used more than once.

(4 points)

> must, mustn't, have to, don't have to, can, can't

0 You _don't have to_ hurry. I'm sure they'll wait for you.

1 Tell Mark and Tony they _____ stay in bed till 9 o'clock if they want. They don't have school today.

2 You _____ get a visa to visit Nepal. But I don't think it's very expensive.

3 I'm afraid you _____ take all your toys with you, girls. The car is too small.

4 The symptoms look very serious. You _____ stay in bed for five days and take these pills three times a day.

5 You _____ bring a friend if you like.

6 Fortunately we _____ take warm clothes with us. It's very hot in Greece at this time of the year.

7 Can't you see the sign, young man? You _____ drive so fast on this road! It's forbidden!

8 You _____ shout at me! I can hear you very well.

B Complete the text with the adjectives given in brackets in the correct form.   (5 points)

There are five people in my family: my parents, Robert, Ana – my (0) _younger_ (young) sister – and me. Robert is (1)_____ (old). He is also (2)_____ (tall) and (3)_____ (intelligent) of us three.

My sister Ana is very smart as well, but certainly (4)_____ (clever) than Robert. Her grades at school are always (5)_____ (bad) than his. Perhaps you will ask about my grades. Well, they are not bad, it's just that I am a bit (6)_____ (lazy) than my brother and sister. For me many other things and activities are (7)_____ (attractive) than learning. Robert is different. He always does his homework, even if it is (8)_____ (boring) thing in the world! But (9)_____ (good) thing about my brother is that he is always ready to help me and Ana with French and German. In fact, he is often (10)_____ (helpful) than our language teachers.

C Complete the sentences with the adjectives in brackets in the correct order.   (2 points)

0 She wants a (black, small) _small black_ handbag for her birthday.

1 Tom always wears formal clothes to work – (wollen, dark, old-fashioned) _____ suits and leather shoes.

2 His new girlfriend has got (big, beautiful, blue) _____ eyes.

3 My sister hates (cheap, nylon) _____ _____ blouses.

4 One day I would like to buy a (small, comfortable, German) _____ car.

D Match the words from the two columns to form words that go together.   (4 points)

0 organic	a)	meat
1 fancy	b)	dress
2 soft	c)	test
3 tender	d)	food
4 mobile	e)	bread
5 home-made	f)	baby
6 driving	g)	drinks
7 new-born	h)	bear
8 polar	i)	phone

0	1	2	3	4	5	6	7	8
d								

E Complete the sentences with the appropriate words. Use only <u>one</u> word in each gap.   (5 points)

0 I hate making __speeches__ . I am just afraid of speaking in public.

1 Chris was very upset because many people didn't turn _____ for his birthday party.

2 A man on his wedding-day or just before it is called a _____ .

3 The only problem is that I don't _____ on with my boss. He is just too difficult to co-operate with.

4 In Britain each child wears a _____ to school – everybody is dressed in the same way.

5 Last year the Oscar _____ for best actress went to Nicole Kidman.

Total ☐ **20**

Test 3 LISTENING

Listen to the radio programme about the Thanksgiving Day in the United States and decide if the statements are true (T) or false (F).

1 ☐ Thanksgiving Day is celebrated on the fourth Thursday in November.

2 ☐ The early colonists arrived in America in the early seventeenth century.

3 ☐ The first thing the colonists learnt was to grow crops.

4 ☐ The first colonists had problems with health.

5 ☐ Indians helped the settlers to learn to fish and hunt.

6 ☐ The settlers didn't feel happy about the crops they gathered in the autumn.

7 ☐ For Thanksgiving Day today American families prepare roast beef.

8 ☐ Because of Thanksgiving Day children have five free days from school.

Total ☐ 8

Test 3 SPEAKING

Work with your partner. Imagine that you want to organise an end-of-year party at school.
Together, plan the party and decide on the following:

• number of people to invite;
• where to hold the party;
• when to hold the party;
• the dress code;
• food and drink;
• entertainment (music, games, etc.);
• how long the party is going to be;
• how to inform people about it;
• how to decorate the room;
• other problems.

Total ☐ 20

Test 4 A USE OF ENGLISH

A Circle the correct alternative in each sentence.

(3 points)

0 Many people believe that in the future television
(will)/is going to disappear.

1 I think you *will/are going to* be very happy if you
marry Leslie.

2 You are learning German at the Goethe Institute.
Will you/Are you going to work for a German
company in the future?

3 There are no clouds in the sky; it *will not/
is not going to* rain.

4 I don't think Mary *will/is going to* make a good
decision if she decides to leave school now.

5 Don't call me in the morning. Since it's Sunday
tomorrow I *will/am going to* stay in bed till
10 o'clock.

6 We are not sure yet but we think we *will/
are going to* emigrate to Canada next year.

B Use the words in the box to complete the sentences.

(4 points)

any, some, no, much, many

0 There are ____no____ oranges in the basket.

1 Can you go and buy _____ chocolate for me?

2 How _____ did you pay for this blouse?

3 I'm very busy at the moment. I'm afraid I've got
_____ time to talk to you.

4 Mark always plays alone. He doesn't have
_____ brothers or sisters.

5 I don't want anything to drink. I think I drank too
_____ tea at home.

6 I'm afraid there are _____ tomatoes left
in the fridge. How _____ do you want me
to buy? Will five be enough?

7 Is there _____ space on the desk for
my books?

C Underline the mistakes in the following sentences and write the correct words or expressions.

(5 points)

0 Robert tried on two pairs of trousers. Unfortunately
both of them suited him. ____neither____

1 I can't buy this dress because there aren't enough
money in my bank account. _____

2 I have broken my left arm again! Fortunately
nothing has happened to my second one.
_____

3 They always have problems with their three children.
Both of them hate eating. _____

4 There is a few eggs in the fridge if you are hungry.
_____

5 He is very selfish and never helps another people.
_____

D Circle the correct alternatives in the text.

(2 points)

I am always (0) *amazing/(amazed)*at how much
teenagers enjoy watching TV. One of my younger
brother's favourite programmes is *Big Brother*. He
believes it is one of the most (1) *fascinating/fascinated*
programmes on TV. When there is nothing to see Tom
gets (2) *depressing/depressed*. Our parents are
(3) *worrying/worried* about him because he spends too
much time in front of the TV screen. However, I think
watching TV is only a (4) *relaxing/relaxed* activity for
Tom. I hope he will soon find a different hobby.

E Complete the sentences with the appropriate words. Use only one word in each gap.

(6 points)

0 We have to pay ____cash____ for the tickets, they
don't accept credit cards.

1 I have a very well-paid job at Computer Electronics
– I _____ about $4,000 a month.

2 A machine that blows hot air on your hair is called
a _____ .

3 I don't _____ any money – I spend all I get
from my parents each month.

4 This photocopier is very _____ to use – you
just press this button and that's it.

5 Richard's grandmother is very generous; she always
gives _____ some money to a charity.

6 Could you _____ me £100, please?
I will give it back to you at the end of the month.

Total | 20

Test 4 B USE OF ENGLISH

A Circle the correct alternative in each sentence.

(3 points)

0 Many people believe that in the future television (will)/is going to disappear.

1 They have worked hard, so they *will/are going to* pass all the exams.

2 I don't think you *will/are going to* make a good decision if you resign from this job.

3 Mary is six months pregnant. She *will/is going to* have a baby in May.

4 I hope every child in Poland *will/is going to* have a computer at home soon.

5 How can you be so sure Carlos *will/is going to* be a doctor? He is still a child.

6 He looks pale. I'm afraid he *will/is going to* faint.

B Use the words in the box to complete the sentences.

(4 points)

any, some, no, much, many

0 There are _____ *no* _____ oranges in the basket.

1 Can I have _____ sugar, please?

2 Is there _____ paper in this drawer?

3 How _____ food do you have to feed your dog every day?

4 If you want to make a cake, you need _____ flour.

5 There aren't _____ apples left. How _____ do you want me to buy? Just four or perhaps more?

6 There is _____ milk in the fridge. The cats have drunk it all.

7 I think you spend too _____ money on clothes.

C Underline the mistakes in the following sentences and write the correct words or expressions.

(5 points)

0 Robert tried on two pairs of trousers. Unfortunately both of them suited him. _____ *neither* _____

1 There aren't much people who like this kind of humour. _____

2 Robin hates two dishes. One is spinach and the another one is roast chicken. _____

3 I have a very big family but the problem is that neither of us likes visiting each other. _____

4 I have a few time so I can help you with your homework. _____

5 My twin brother and I are very similar. All of us have brown eyes and fair hair. _____

D Circle the correct alternatives in the text.

(2 points)

All my friends are (0) (fascinating)/fascinated people. One of them, Bob, is very (1) *interesting/interested* in the cinema. He goes to the cinema four times a week and never gets (2) *boring/bored*. It is (3) *amazing/amazed* how he can remember all the films after seeing so many of them. Before the Oscar ceremony he is very (4) *exciting/excited* and stays up all night to watch it.

E Complete the sentences with the appropriate words. Use only one word in each gap.

(6 points)

0 We have to pay _____ *cash* _____ for the tickets. They don't accept credit cards.

1 I never _____ more than $100 from one person and try to give the money back as soon as possible.

2 The carpet is all dirty. Take a _____ cleaner and clean it, please.

3 I asked for a 20% _____ but I didn't get it and had to pay the full price.

4 My palmtop computer is not very _____ – it breaks down very often.

5 We got $1,000 as a wedding gift and decided to put it _____ our bank account.

6 Do you have any change? I need some coins for a cola-machine and I've got only one twenty-pound _____ .

Total	20

Test 4 READING

Read the text and decide if the statements are true (T) or false (F).

1 ☐ The American Gold Rush started in the second half of the nineteenth century.

2 ☐ The pieces of metal found in the river were yellow.

3 ☐ James W. Marshall didn't show the gold he found to his boss.

4 ☐ People travelled to California by horse, ship and on foot.

5 ☐ The huts in which people lived near the river were usually made of bricks.

6 ☐ The owners of hotels, bars and restaurants got really rich in California.

7 ☐ In 1897 gold was discovered in Canada.

8 ☐ Today people can look for gold in California near Sacramento.

The American Gold Rush

It all started early in 1848 in California. James W. Marshall was working by the riverside when he found some small pieces of yellow metal in the water. He showed them to his boss. It was gold. The two men tried to keep this discovery a secret but without success. Soon, the magic word 'gold' was repeated all around the world.

Everybody wanted to go to California to get rich. Thousands of people started to rush to the golden river by horse, by ship and even on foot. Night after night, a few more new towns appeared along the river. Some people brought tents to live in while others built wooden houses called huts. Looking for gold was hard work and many people were disappointed. Only the lucky ones found gold – sometimes up to $2,000 in one day.

It is not surprising that many small hotels, restaurants and bars opened in the new towns. Their owners made fortunes providing services to people who arrived in town in search of gold.

By the end of 1850, the California Gold Rush was over. However, about forty-seven years later gold was discovered again, this time in Canada. Once more, over a thousand people left their homes and families to look for a better future.

Today, at the original site of the California Gold Rush, near Sacramento, visitors can still try their luck with finding the yellow pieces of metal in the river. The old buildings have been redecorated and tourists can experience the life of the old days. Many of them are sure that they can find at least a small bit of gold.

Total ☐ 8

Test 4 WRITING

Write an advert for a gadget for sale, and:

• write what the object is and describe it briefly;
• mention some of its advantages;
• say how long you have used it and give its price;
• give your contact details.

Total ☐ 20

Test B LISTENING

Listen to a short lecture about the history of money and decide if the statements are true (T) or false (F).

1 ☐ The exchange of goods was the first form of payment.

2 ☐ Metal bars were first used as a form of payment in ancient Egypt.

3 ☐ The first coins appeared in the sixth century BC.

4 ☐ The value of the first coins did not depend on the metal content.

5 ☐ The banknotes were introduced in the eighteenth century.

6 ☐ It is possible that in the future people will buy goods only via computers.

Total ☐ **6**

Test B SPEAKING

Student A
Look at the photograph and answer the questions.

1 Do the people in the picture enjoy the shopping? Why do you think so?

2 What are the good and bad points of doing the shopping in a supermarket?

Total ☐ **20**

Student B
Look at the photograph and answer the questions.

1 Do the girls in the picture often go shopping? Why do you think so?

2 Do you like going shopping in shopping malls? Why/Why not?

Total ☐ **20**

Test B READING

Read the text about the pubs in Great Britain and decide which answer is correct, a, b or c.

1 There are nearly 7,000 pubs
   a in Great Britain.
   b in Europe.
   c in the capital of England.

2 In a pub, you can
   a have a meal.
   b stay there until 1 a.m.
   c sing karaoke songs.

3 In a pub, you are not allowed to
   a watch TV.
   b read newspapers.
   c stay there after midnight.

4 When you come to a pub, it is important to
   a order a drink.
   b bring a friend (old or young).
   c sing to the music you hear.

5 'The Red Lion' is
   a a name of a pub.
   b a game you can play in a pub.
   c the name of a band which gives live concerts
       in pubs.

6 There are _____ signals to go home.
   a two
   b three
   c four

Pubs in Great Britain

People say that pubs are as important as museums in Great Britain. Their long history has played a big role shaping the customs and culture of this country but they have also become very popular in other European countries and all over the world.

English public houses or pubs are one of the characteristic features of British life. They are visited by members of every social class, both young and old, men and women. In London alone, there are nearly seven thousand pubs. Going to a different one every night for a 'pint of beer' would take you around twenty years.

The most popular name for a pub is 'The Red Lion'. You can find several types of beer, gin, rum and other drinks. You can eat a little, play darts, billiards or discuss events of the day. In many pubs you can even watch sports programmes. Some pubs offer live music to listen to.

At present, there are about seventy-three thousand pubs in Great Britain. Many of them date back to the seventeenth or eighteenth century. All of them offer new guests a warm welcome and a nice, friendly atmosphere. There are, however, a few rules which you must follow. For example, you should always order a drink in a pub. You should also know when to leave. There are always two bells to warn you to finish your drink – at 10.50 p.m. and at 11.00 p.m. You must leave the pub by 11.20 p.m.

Total	6

Test B WRITING

Write an email to your classmates and invite them to your birthday party. Tell them:

- when and where it is going to take place;
- what food and drinks there will be;
- the dress code;
- how to get to your place.

Total	20

Mid-year Test A USE OF ENGLISH

A Find the mistakes in the following sentences and rewrite the sentences correctly. (10 points)

0 What does she do at the moment?

  What is she doing at the moment?

1 We have gone to Mexico three times.

  _____

  _____

2 My sister is a journalist and she is interviewing many people.

  _____

  _____

3 I usually have some sandwiches and the glass of orange juice for breakfast.

  _____

  _____

4 When I was a child I was playing football every Sunday.

  _____

  _____

5 The animals are hungry because I haven't already fed them.

  _____

  _____

6 That's OK. I don't mind to open the window.

  _____

  _____

7 Stop it, boys! I am tired with you making so much noise!

  _____

  _____

8 I don't have breakfast in the morning. I just have shower and go quickly to work.

  _____

  _____

9 Where have you bought this cotton wonderful black shirt?

  _____

  _____

10 I'm sorry, but Mr Smith mustn't see you right now. He is talking to another client.

  _____

  _____

B Put the verbs in brackets in the correct tense. (8 points)

0 My grandmother ____*gave*____ (give) me this ring ten years ago.

1 I _____ (not believe) he is only twenty-five. He must be older.

2 George _____ (break) his leg twice last year.

3 I'm sorry but Dr Harris is not here. He never _____ (work) in the mornings.

4 The sky is very clear. It _____ (be) a beautiful day.

5 She looks very sad. I think that's because her boyfriend _____ (leave) her.

6 John, this is Mark. We _____ (do) the same course at the university.

7 The teacher saw them while they _____ (kiss) in front of the school.

8 I hope I _____ (have) more time for my hobbies next year.

C Circle the correct alternative in each sentence. (4 points)

0 I'm not really *interesting/interested* in politics.

1 Can you imagine *to live/living* in the nineteenth century without television and mobile phones?

2 One of my legs is a bit shorter than *another/the other*.

3 I don't really like listening to *music/the music*.

4 There *is/are* many things I would like to do in the future.

5 *None/Neither* of my three brothers and two sisters are keen on sport.

6 You *mustn't/don't have to* put on your evening dress. The occasion is not very formal.

7 We are all very tall, but Jane is *taller/the tallest* of us.

8 You don't really need *many/a lot of* money to organise a trip to Africa.

D Match the words from the two columns to form correct English expressions. (3 points)

0 to fail	a) a decision
1 to grow	b) glass
2 to recycle	c) casually
3 to do	d) a driving test
4 to make	e) a uniform
5 to wear	f) plants
6 to dress	g) exercise

0	1	2	3	4	5	6
d						

E Write the words or expressions from the box under the correct headings. Then add three more words or expressions to each list. (8 points)

election, house-warming, clear the table, discount

HOUSEWORK:

_____

POLITICS:

_____

TYPES OF PARTIES:

_____

MONEY:

_____

F Complete the sentences with the appropriate adjectives. The first letter of each adjective is given. (7 points)

0 A ____busy____ person has many things to do all the time.

1 Tom is very h_____ . You can always leave your money with him.

2 I don't like the taste of beer, it's just too b_____ for me.

3 Elderly people are usually very w_____ . You can learn a lot from them.

4 The new type of palmtop is very c_____ . You can carry it in your handbag.

5 My father does not panic easily. Even in the worst crisis he always stays c_____ .

6 I have had enough of discos and parties. I'm dreaming of a quiet, p_____ evening at home.

7 Your spaghetti was very good, only the cheese was too m_____ . Next time you should buy one with a stronger taste.

Total	40

Mid-year Test B USE OF ENGLISH

A Find the mistakes in the following sentences and rewrite the sentences correctly. (10 points)

0 What does she do at the moment?

What is she doing at the moment?

1 This month I didn't spend any money on clothes.

_____

_____

2 My older sister always wears old horrible dark brown sweaters.

_____

_____

3 I met her when she walked in the park with her two children.

_____

_____

4 People who are good in playing chess are usually also good mathematicians.

_____

_____

5 I enjoy to listen to classical music. In fact, I don't listen to anything else.

_____

_____

6 Don't forget to close a door when you leave the room.

_____

_____

7 This pizza is smelling very good.

_____

_____

8 She once a week plays basketball with a local team.

_____

_____

9 My boss stays at the work very long on Mondays.

_____

_____

10 You mustn't tell me what to buy. I have a shopping list.

_____

_____

B Put the verbs in brackets in the correct tense. (8 points)

0 My grandmother _____gave_____ (give) me this ring 10 years ago.

1 Isn't she hungry? She _____ (not eat) anything all day.

2 I'm not sure yet but I think I _____ (study) medicine in the future.

3 Please, stop talking! Can't you see? I _____ (revise) for my English exam.

4 Our teacher _____ (not hear) the terrible news yet.

5 I don't understand why my children always _____ (make) the same mistakes.

6 Were you sleeping when I _____ (call) you?

7 Look at the roof of that building! The man _____ (jump) in a second.

8 In 1994 she _____ (leave) Spain and went to live in England.

C Circle the correct alternative in each sentence. (4 points)

0 I'm not really *interesting/(interested)* in politics.

1 When you go to church you *must/have to* switch off your mobile phone.

2 There are two kinds of meat I never eat: one is beef and *the second/the other* lamb.

3 If you are tired in the morning, you should avoid *to watch/watching* TV late at night.

4 Mum, let me help you with *a/the* suitcase. It's too heavy for you.

5 John is in a very difficult situation but my situation is *worse/the worst*.

6 We could organise a party for four people with some drinks and *a little/a few* food.

7 My two best friends love jogging, but *both/neither* of them likes aerobics.

8 *Is/Are* there anything you would like to change in your school?

D Match the words from the two columns to form correct English expressions. (3 points)

0 to fail	a) repairs
1 to tie up	b) long hair
2 to receive	c) badly
3 to sleep	d) a driving test
4 to make	e) formal clothes
5 to wear	f) bad news
6 to do	g) a speech

0	1	2	3	4	5	6
d						

E Write the words or expressions from the box under the correct headings. Then add three more words or expressions to each list. (8 points)

> cottage, plumber, overrated, loan

NEGATIVE OPINION ADJECTIVES:

_____

BANKS:

_____

TYPES OF HOUSES:

_____

JOBS:

_____

F Complete the sentences with appropriate adjectives. The first letter of each adjective is given. (7 points)

0 A _____busy_____ person has many things to do all the time.

1 My wife calls me a workaholic but I'm just a h_____ person.

2 Her new computer is not very r_____ ; it breaks down very often.

3 Hungarian food is rather s_____ . My brother doesn't like it, it's just too hot for him.

4 John loves all kinds of sports programmes because he is a very a_____ person himself; he practises judo, karate, and he also plays football.

5 My little daughter was very b_____ at the dentist. She didn't cry at all.

6 Is your meat t_____ ? Mine is tough.

7 Barbara is not very d_____ . She always thinks for hours before choosing what to do.

Total | **40**

Mid-year Test LISTENING

Listen to the humorous description of driving cars in England and decide if the statements are true (T) or false (F).

1 ☐ In English towns you can drive your car as fast as thirty miles per hour.

2 ☐ It is very easy to recognise a police car in England.

3 ☐ There is usually one policeman in a police car.

4 ☐ You have to leave the lights on when you park your car at night.

5 ☐ The policemen do not always know where you can park your car.

6 ☐ You are allowed to park your car in the West End of London.

Total ☐ 6

Mid-year Test SPEAKING

Imagine that a few days ago you won £100 in a lottery and you want to share it with your partner. However, you need different things. Think why you need them because you have to convince the other person about them. Together decide what you want to spend the money on.

Student A

- a new computer game
- a pair of jeans
- tickets to a rock concert
- tickets to the disco
- a personal stereo
- a new alarm clock

Total ☐ 20

Student B

- a science fiction book
- a new CD of their favourite singer
- a pair of sports shoes
- tickets to a basketball match
- birthday party at McDonald's
- a dog

Total ☐ 20

Mid-year Test WRITING

Write a description of a sports event you have seen recently. Look at the options below and choose one event. Divide your text into four paragraphs.

OPTIONS

a football match   a car race   a swimming competition   a dance tournament

Write:
- why, when and where the event took place;
- who took part in it and how they looked;
- when and how it started;
- who went with you to see it;
- how you felt before and after the event;
- what you did, ate and drank at the event;
- when and how the party finished;
- how you got home.

Useful linking words:
before, after, when, as soon as, later, firstly, while, after that, suddenly, next, then, finally, in the end

Total ☐ 20

Mid-year Test READING

Read the article about the history of coffee drinking and circle the correct answer, a, b or c.

1 Coffee was discovered
   a in Europe.
   b in Africa.
   c in Asia.

2 Coffee drinking was popularised by
   a the Ethiopians.
   b the Italians.
   c the Turks.

3 Coffee was first grown
   a in Italy.
   b in Turkey.
   c in Yemen.

4 In Europe, coffee was popular as
   a a medicine.
   b the wine of Islam.
   c a natural stimulant.

5 By the end of the sixteenth century people drank coffee
   a in northern Europe.
   b in the most important European cities.
   c in Paris and London only.

6 New brands of coffee
   a are as harmful as the original mocca.
   b are less harmful than regular coffee.
   c may influence our concentration ability.

Time for coffee

The story of coffee drinking is one of the greatest and most fascinating in history. Millions of coffee drinkers worldwide cannot imagine life without a cup of aromatic coffee in the morning. Coffee is a natural stimulant which makes us feel more awake, alert and ready to concentrate.

The qualities of mocca, as coffee was once known, were first discovered in Ethiopia more than one thousand years ago. However, it was not Africans but Turks and Arabs who actively encouraged coffee drinking. The habit of coffee drinking quickly spread throughout the Arab world, where coffee won a reputation as the wine of Islam.

Coffee was first grown in Yemen. It was popular with Turks who served the drink to visiting Italian merchants. In 1615 traders from Venice brought coffee to Europe, where it was originally sold as a medicine. By the end of the sixteenth century coffee was drunk in major European cities from Paris to London. Now, around the world there are different methods of preparing coffee, for example, in Turkey coffee is traditionally boiled three times while Italians are the inventors of espresso and cappuccino.

We drink coffee because of its aroma, taste and stimulating effect. However, extensive consumption of coffee may be harmful to our health, for instance, it may increase one's blood pressure or make one's heart beat irregularly. Fortunately, new brands of coffee have been appearing on the market recently. As they do not contain substances harmful to health, many people will not have to give up their coffee-drinking habits.

Total	6

Test 5 A USE OF ENGLISH

A Complete these conditional sentences with the verbs in the correct tense. (8 points)

0 If they ____ate____ (eat) less, they wouldn't be so fat.

1 If she wanted to be my friend, she _____ (visit) me more often.

2 If she _____ (have) a free evening tomorrow, she will take both of you to the cinema.

3 If it were cheaper, I _____ (go) on holiday to Turkey.

4 If you heat water to 100 degrees centigrade, it _____ (boil).

5 I would phone her if I _____ (know) her telephone number.

6 She can help you if you _____ (ask) her.

7 My mum would be very sad if you _____ (not come) to visit us.

8 If you _____ (not water) plants regularly, they die.

B Put the words in the correct order to make sentences. (2 points)

0 start/often/work/at/I/9 a.m.

   I often start work at 9 a.m.

1 grandma/slowly/my/normally/walks/very

   _____

2 is/our/Fiona/definitely/singer/best

   _____

3 hard/listen/I/understand/tried/to/but/could/I/ anything/hardly

   _____

4 is/well/Tom/player/and/a/usually/very/good/plays/he

   _____

C Fill in the gaps in the sentences with *make* or *do*. (3 points)

0 Do you think I could use your mobile phone to ____make____ a phone call to my parents?

1 If you don't know the answer try to _____ a guess.

2 I can't go with you now, I have to _____ the dishes first.

3 Do you _____ any sports?

4 Don't worry! We all _____ mistakes when we start learning a foreign language.

5 Ann is very reserved and she finds it very difficult to _____ new friends.

6 Would you like me to _____ a cup of tea for you?

D Write the words to form compound nouns. (3 points)

0 detective ____drama____

1 search _____

2 chat _____

3 nature _____

E Complete the text with one word in each gap. (4 points)

I just hate listening (0) ____to____ other people's conversations on the phone. I simply can't understand why so many people answer their mobile phone when someone rings them (1) _____ on the bus or at the bank. They should (2) _____ it off in the first place or if they have forgotten to do that, they should at least hang (3) _____ very quickly. I don't mind if they (4) _____ on to the Net and use their multimedia mobiles to play games. This really doesn't bother me – of course if they do that with the sound off!

Total | **20**

Test 5 B USE OF ENGLISH

A Complete these conditional sentences with the verbs in the correct tense. (8 points)

0 If they _____ate_____ (eat) less, they wouldn't be so fat.

1 If you walk ten miles with me, you _____ (feel) tired.

2 If I won the lottery, I _____ (buy) a beautiful house.

3 You would feel better if you _____ (drink) a cup of hot tea.

4 I won't go out if it _____ (not stop) raining.

5 If the temperature is lower than 0 degrees centigrade, water _____ (freeze).

6 We would take you to the concert if we _____ (have) more tickets.

7 You can waste of lot of time if you _____ (watch) too much TV.

8 I _____ (not help) her even if she asked me.

B Put the words in the correct order to make sentences. (2 points)

0 start/often/work/at/I/9 a.m.

I often start work at 9 a.m.

1 seen/have/recently/Mark/you/?

_____

2 certainly/he/write/will/soon/back

_____

3 always/I/very/drive/carefully

_____

4 works/hardly/she/but/any/hard/money/earns

_____

C Fill in the gaps in the sentences with *make* or *do*. (3 points)

0 Do you think I could use your mobile phone to _____make_____ a phone call to my parents?

1 I'm afraid you should stop watching TV and _____ your homework instead.

2 Can I _____ a suggestion? I think we should write this letter again.

3 There is nothing to eat at home. We need to _____ the shopping.

4 Don't worry. I'm sure you will _____ very well in your new school.

5 I don't want to _____ any predictions about his future.

6 It's not fair! My sisters never _____ the washing-up.

D Write the words to form compound nouns. (3 points)

0 detective _____drama_____

1 reference _____

2 soap _____

3 quiz _____

E Complete the text with one word in each gap. (4 points)

I hate getting (0) _____up_____ early but my friends seem to forget this. They often ring me (1) _____ at 6 o'clock in the morning to ask about something unimportant. Half asleep, I (2) _____ on the light and (3) _____ up the phone. When I hear the voice of one of my friends I just hang (4) _____ and go back to sleep. If it is something really important, they will call me later!

Total | **20**

Test 5 LISTENING

Listen to the interview with a teacher who is talking about the role of computers in education and decide if the statements are true (T) or false (F).

1 ☐ At school, computers are useful only in the language lessons.

2 ☐ Students can find examples of real-life communication on the Internet.

3 ☐ It takes a long time to find online publications.

4 ☐ It is not easy to check the meaning of new words on the Internet websites.

5 ☐ You can present your opinions on various topics over the Internet.

6 ☐ Teachers may find it difficult to find lesson plans in the Net.

7 ☐ Teachers can find collections of exercises on the Internet.

8 ☐ It is easy to make students learn new things using computers.

Total | **8**

Test 5 SPEAKING

Work with your partner. One of you is for the use of computers in everyday life and the other person is against it. Talk to your partner and try to convince him/her about your beliefs.

Student A
Arguments for the use of computers in everyday life

- computers in every house – make housework easy – plan the use of energy and water – lower payments
- computers in banks and homes – do financial operations without using money
- Internet – do the shopping without going to shops – no waste of time
- cars driven by computer pilots – plan journeys without traffic jams – choose shortest distances
- computers and crime – help find criminals (by publishing their descriptions and photos), stolen cars and property
- computers in schools and education – possibilities to use Internet pages to get information about various things
- more time for leisure activities – buy cinema tickets without queueing – even watch films on computers

Total | **20**

Student B
Arguments against the use of computers in everyday life

- computers at home – people sit at home no meetings with others
- no control over crime – terrorists – communicate over Internet
- hackers – steal information – plant viruses
- too much time spent on playing games
- shopping – no possibility to try clothes on
- computers and health – back pains, problems with sight

Total | **20**

Test 6 A USE OF ENGLISH

A Put the verbs in brackets into the Present Simple, the Present Perfect or the Past Simple.

(6 points)

0 I ____worked____ (work) very hard when I was in Paris.

1 I _____ (hate) cats since I was a child.

2 She can't help you now, she _____ (have) other things to do.

3 For the last fifteen years my parents _____ (live) in Sydney, Australia.

4 Emily Dickinson _____ (write) many well-known poems.

5 Both my grandparents died about ten years ago. They _____ (love) each other very much.

6 Steven is very thirsty. He _____ (not drink) anything all day.

B Read the text and circle the correct alternatives.

(6 points)

The Eaton Hotel (0) *situated/(is situated)* in the very centre of London, near Victoria Station. It (1) *built/ was built* in 1980, just before I (2) *visited/have visited* England for the second time. At first, the hotel (3) *had/has had* only five single rooms but later, in 1983, it (4) *changed/was changed* by its owners into a bigger bed and breakfast place. It is now a very modern and comfortable hotel. Breakfast (5) *serves/ is served* between 7 and 9 o'clock and the food is always very tasty. The rooms (6) *clean/are cleaned* every day and the chambermaids who work there (7) *change/are changed* the towels every time you ask them. Apart from the excellent food and comfortable rooms the hotel (8) *offers/has offered* some other services now. Very early in the morning or late at night visitors (9) *are met/have been met* at the airport by one of the hotel staff and then they (10) *take/are taken* directly to the hotel. I (11) *stayed/have stayed* in the Eaton Hotel twice so far and each time I (12) *have looked after/have been looked after* very well. I think I can recommend the Eaton Hotel to visitors to London without any reservations.

C Match the words from the two columns to form compound words.

(3 points)

0 changeable	a) environment
1 body	b) surfing
2 cross-country	c) diving
3 scuba	d) weather
4 natural	e) cold
5 political	f) skiing
6 freezing	g) problems

0	1	2	3	4	5	6
d						

D Complete the sentences with the appropriate words. The first letter of each word is given.

(5 points)

0 Many people emigrate to other countries to ____avoid____ paying high taxes.

1 The f_____ last year were started by heavy rainfall in the mountains.

2 Only two experienced climbers managed to reach the s_____ of Giewont.

3 It's very dangerous to ski here in winter. Three skiers are still missing after today's a_____ .

4 Please, drive very slowly. It is very f_____ today and you can't see clearly.

5 When Mount Erebus erupted many people were killed and thousands more lost their houses in the e_____ that followed the eruption.

Total	20

Test 6 B USE OF ENGLISH

A Put the verbs in brackets into the Present Simple, the Present Perfect or the Past Simple.

(6 points)

0 I ___worked___ (work) very hard when I was in Paris.

1 Chopin _____ (compose) a lot of wonderful music.

2 Tom is my best friend. I _____ (know) him for two years now.

3 He _____ (do) some sightseeing in Chile for two weeks, then he flew to Peru.

4 My teacher _____ (not understand) why we are so often late for school .

5 My mother is really happy because she _____ (pass) her driving test.

6 We _____ (move) to Warsaw when I was a small child.

B Read the text and circle the correct alternatives.

(6 points)

Prima Pasta restaurant (0) *situated*/*is situated* in Little Italy in New York. I (1) *had/have had* dinner there three times so far and each time the food (2) *was/has been* excellent. At first, the restaurant (3) *served/has served* only four different kinds of pasta but later, in 1995, it (4) *changed/was changed* by its owners into a very big pasta and pizza place. Now, apart from a variety of pasta it (5) *offers/is offered* twelve kinds of pizza and many other Italian dishes. Pasta shapes (6) *include/are included* penne, tagliatelle, fusilli and rigatoni. The staff (cooks, waitresses and waiters) are very competent and you can see that they (7) *have chosen/have been chosen* carefully. The food (8) *always serves/is always served* hot and tasty and customers (9) *never wait/have never waited* longer than fifteen minutes for their dishes. Actually, when I (10) *was/have been* at Prima Pasta for the second time, our meal (11) *brought/was brought* after twenty minutes. The waitress was very sorry for the delay and we (12) *gave/were given* our pizzas completely free of charge.

C Match the words from the two columns to form compound words.

(3 points)

0	changeable	a)	jumping
1	natural	b)	hot
2	jet	c)	plate
3	boiling	d)	weather
4	ice	e)	skating
5	ski	f)	skiing
6	continental	g)	disasters

0	1	2	3	4	5	6
d						

D Complete the sentences with the appropriate words. The first letter of each word is given.

(5 points)

0 Many people emigrate to other countries to ___avoid___ paying high taxes.

1 A d_____ is a long period of time with no rain.

2 In the distance we saw the snow-covered p_____ of the Tatra Mountains.

3 Last year there was not enough food in Ethiopia and many people died during the terrible f_____ .

4 Oh, come on! Let's go for a walk. It's not rain, it's just light d_____ .

5 A large mass of ice which moves very slowly down a mountain valley is called a g_____ .

Total	20

Test 6 READING

Read the text about the pirates. Then match the paragraph titles (A–I) with the paragraphs (1–8).
There is one extra title.

Pirates

1 ___ When you hear the word *pirate*, you probably see a man with a wooden leg, a piece of black cloth over one eye, dressed in seventeenth-century clothes. On his shoulder, there is a parrot. Most likely, you can picture him standing next to a box full of treasure under a palm tree somewhere on a desert island.

2 ___ A pirate was a bandit who sailed the seas in search of ships carrying valuable things.

3 ___ Almost all of the pirates' ships flew the famous Jolly Roger which was a black flag with a skull and two white bones on it.

4 ___ When a pirate got on a ship, he stole everything and killed the sailors.

5 ___ Then he sold the stolen goods in the nearest port and spent all the money on various forms of entertainment, usually on drinking beer and rum.

6 ___ However, the pirates were very disciplined. There was order and discipline on their ships because they wanted their actions to be successful. Some pirates did not obey the rules and they were punished in a cruel way.

7 ___ Pirates did not spend all the money they stole. Often, they buried the treasure in some distant place so that it was very difficult to find for many years. Many treasure boxes were never found.

8 ___ Watch out! Maybe the next time you walk along the beach you will step on something big and heavy?

A ACTIONS AFTER GETTING ON A SHIP
B JOB
C DISCIPLINE ON SHIPS
D USE OF STOLEN MONEY
E APPEARANCE
F PIRATES' PRIVATE LIFE
G CHANCES TO FIND TREASURE
H PIRATE SYMBOLS
I HIDING THE TREASURE

Total   8

Test 6 WRITING

You have decided to go to the mountains in Scotland for a few days. Write a formal letter to the travel agency (about 100–150 words) to find out:

• if they organise trips to Scottish mountains;
• how long the trips are;
• what kind of accommodation they are offering;
• how you will pay;
• if they can book a place in a youth hostel;
• if they offer a student discount.

Total   20

Test C LISTENING

Listen to an extract from a geography lesson – a mini-lecture about the Dead Sea – and circle the appropriate answer, a, b or c.

1 The Dead Sea lies _____ kilometres away from Jerusalem.
   a 24
   b 34
   c 44

2 The Dead Sea is_____ kilometres long.
   a 24
   b 34
   c 74

3 Over the years the Dead Sea has changed
   a its rich flora and its climate.
   b its climate and its size.
   c its size and its rich flora.

4 In 1 litre of the Dead Sea water there is _____ 327 grams of salt.
   a about
   b exactly
   c more than

5 The highest recorded temperature for the Dead Sea region is _____ degrees centigrade.
   a 51
   b 14
   c 34

6 The plan to join the Dead Sea with the Mediterranean has been put aside because of
   a the lack of time
   b the lack of money
   c the lack of investors

Total	6

Test C SPEAKING

You and your friend have won a fantastic holiday this summer. Discuss the information about each holiday below. Then decide where you want to go and why.

Sea cruise
- six days
- spacious, comfortable ship
- three meals a day
- swimming pool
- all-night discos
- many unknown people
- a lot of noise
- sea-sickness
- limited space

Beach holiday
- three weeks
- self-catering flats
- only breakfasts and dinners
- two excursions to famous places of interest
- rent-a-car service
- high temperature
- many insects

Total	20

Test C READING

Read the article about the hackers. Then match the paragraph titles (A–G) with the paragraphs (1–6). There is one extra title.

Hackers

1 ___ With the development of technology in the twenty-first century, it would be really difficult to imagine life without computers. They are a source of information, education and entertainment. But today's world of computers can also be quite frightening and dangerous. This is because of people who use computers for illegal purposes. They are called hackers.

2 ___ Hackers spend their time playing with computer data in all parts of cyberspace. Much of what they do is not dangerous, but sometimes their activities break the law, for example, when they break into websites, take control of computers or create viruses. They are especially interested in breaking through the security of military websites.

3 ___ Hackers know how to trick people just using their programs. They use a 'Trojan Horse', a program that looks perfectly safe, but actually contains something destructive. The only way of not getting into trouble is not to open it.

4 ___ Although they can be seriously punished if they are caught, most hackers still think that what they do is a game. They often meet at festivals to take part in discussions, share their experiences, meet other hackers and generally to have a good time.

5 ___ These meetings are organised in well-known places like Las Vegas or Berlin. However, what the hackers do at such festivals is a secret and often many of their activities take place at night.

6 ___ Recently, hacking has started to increase. Hackers are getting into computer systems and stealing or destroying information. It is certain that there will be a lot more of this high-tech crime in the twenty-first century.

A HACKERS' CRIMINAL ACTIVITIES
B HACKING IN THE FUTURE
C HACKERS' SOCIAL ACTIVITIES
C SPECIALIST PROGRAMS
E THE ROLE OF COMPUTERS IN EVERYDAY LIFE
F AVOIDING COMPUTER VIRUSES
G PLACES WHERE HACKERS MEET

Total | 6

Test C WRITING

Imagine you and your friends are members of a new fan club – Computer Game Lovers. As you want to make it popular on the Internet, plan and write an Internet page describing your club. Write:

- why and when the club started;
- how long it has existed on the Internet;
- who the people in charge of the club are and what they do;
- number of members joining the club weekly/monthly;
- information you can find on the club website;
- who can join the club;
- requirements for joining the club;
- other information.

Total | 20

Test 7 A USE OF ENGLISH

A Put the verbs in brackets into the Present Simple, the Present Continuous, the Simple Future or the structure *to be going to* to express future events.

(8 points)

0 I can't come tomorrow, I __am meeting__ (meet) Mr Smith after work.

1 My train _____ (leave) Budapest at 5.15 p.m.

2 Have you heard the news? Beth and Steven _____ (get) married in June.

3 I'll call you as soon as I _____ (return) from Berlin.

4 I'm sure she _____ (not do) anything this evening. You can ask her out.

5 OK, Dad. I _____ (answer) the phone this time.

6 Don't forget to take the dog for a walk before you _____ (leave) for school.

7 Don't worry. I _____ (help) you with your homework if you like.

8 He _____ (not give) up smoking next year. That's not his intention at all.

B Complete the sentences with question tags.

(5 points)

0 They are studying history, __aren't they__ ?

1 He doesn't like you, _____ ?

2 You went there yesterday, _____ ?

3 She won't be late for our meeting, _____ ?

4 They haven't done it yet, _____ ?

5 You can come at 5 p.m., _____ ?

C Read the text below and think of the word which best fits each gap. Use only _one_ word in each gap. The first letter of each word is provided.

(4 points)

Yesterday we went to the (0) __concert__ of country and western music at the Festival Hall. I was really impressed by the guitarist who gave a (1) b_____ performance. I also liked the fact that the members of the band played many musical instruments: acoustic and electric guitars, drums, the piano and the (2) v_____ . My boyfriend's impressions were not so good though. He said he couldn't hear anything because the quality of the sound was very (3) p_____ . He also expected more new hits from his favourite band so for him the concert was really (4) d_____ .

D Complete the sentences with one word in each gap. Then rewrite the sentences changing the underlined verbs.

(3 points)

0 The doctor told me to __give__ __up__ smoking immediately!

The doctor told me to stop smoking immediately !

1 I __came__ _____ this dress in a second-hand shop.

_____ .

2 Many people who lose their jobs nowadays decide to _____ __up__ their own companies.

_____ .

3 John has __taken__ _____ judo only recently but he is quite good at it.

_____ .

Total	20

Test 7 B USE OF ENGLISH

A Put the verbs in brackets into the Present Simple, the Present Continuous, the Simple Future or the structure *to be going to* to express future events.

(8 points)

0 I can't come tomorrow, I __am meeting__ (meet) Mr Smith after work.

1 In the New Year I _____ (learn) how to play the piano.

2 When he _____ (find) a better job, they'll rent a bigger flat.

3 Fine, I _____ (clean) the windows today. But it's the last time!

4 Monday is not a good time for our meeting. She _____ (fly) to Paris tomorrow for two weeks.

5 We will celebrate after you _____ (pass) all your exams.

6 You don't have to hurry. Her plane _____ (arrive) at Heathrow Airport after midnight.

7 I will talk to you as soon as I _____ (come) home from work.

8 We _____ (not do) anything after 5 p.m. Let's go to the cinema!

B Complete the sentences with question tags.

(5 points)

0 They are studying history, __aren't they__ ?

1 He has already finished his project, _____ ?

2 It isn't very expensive, _____ ?

3 You will be able to come, _____ ?

4 They told us the truth, _____ ?

5 You don't really believe it, _____ ?

C Read the text below and think of the word which best fits each gap. Use only <u>one</u> word in each gap. The first letter of each word is provided.

(4 points)

My friend Eve loves dancing so yesterday we decided to go to a (0) __nightclub__ . We chose The Star, which has three big dancing (1) f_____ and is famous for very good music played by Mark – the best (2) d_____ in our city. The name of the club comes from the shape of the stage. The stage (3) d_____ is spectacular and really original. We didn't dance much because we met an old friend and wanted to talk to him. We could hardly hear him because the music was loud and (4) d_____ . In the end, we decided to go to a quite, peaceful place for a chat.

D Complete the sentences with one word in each gap. Then rewrite the sentences changing the underlined verbs.

(3 points)

0 The doctor told me to __give__ __up__ smoking immediately!

   The doctor told me to stop smoking immediately !

1 She might feel __left__ _____ because we haven't invited her to our wedding.

   _____ .

2 Of course, I'll be there on time! I would hate to _____ __out on__ the opening ceremony.

   _____ .

3 His career developed very quickly. He _started_ _____ as a junior assistant only three years ago and now he is the manager.

   _____ .

Total 20

Test 7 LISTENING

Listen to the interview with Rik Palieri and circle the correct answer, a, b or c.

1 When he was a teenager, Rik was interested in
   a folk music.
   b rock music.
   c jazz.

2 The first instrument that he learnt to play was
   a a guitar.
   b bagpipes.
   c a banjo.

3 In *National Geographic* Rik saw a photo of
   a a banjo.
   b a guitar.
   c a set of bagpipes.

4 Rik went to Poland in 1980 to
   a participate in a music festival.
   b buy bagpipes.
   c study.

5 In 1980, Rik stayed in Poland for
   a a year.
   b half a year.
   c a month.

6 In Poland Rik learnt to
   a communicate in the country's language.
   b take care of sheep dogs.
   c play a banjo.

7 Going back to America, Rik took
   a a folk costume.
   b a dog.
   c a book of traditions of the mountain people.

8 What Rik finds important is
   a his performances.
   b travelling to foreign countries.
   c folk traditions.

Total	8

Test 7 SPEAKING

You want to join a dance group in the local community centre. Talk to the dance teacher in the club and find out what you should do to join the group. Your partner will play the role of the dance teacher. Now read the information below.

Student A
Student

Age	15 next month
Abilities	play the guitar
	feel the rhythm
	good at imitating movements
Experience	practised jive and rock 'n' roll with a friend two years ago
Attitude	eager to train a lot
	love to dance
Dreams	to join the dance club
	to learn to dance modern disco dances to take part in a dancing competition (and win the main prize if possible)
Ask about	type of dances taught
	time and place of lessons
	clothes to wear at lessons
	price of the lessons

Total	20

Student B
Dance Teacher

Course	classical dances like waltz, tango
	modern dances like rap, hip hop
	preparation for a dance competition
	Mon., Wed., Fri., 5–6 p.m.
	£30 a month
Requirements	age – over 15
	clothes – training costume and light sports shoes
	experience – none
	other – punctuality
Ask about	experience in dancing
	musical interests
	physical fitness and sports practice
	ability to play musical instruments
	reason for joining the dance group

Total	20

Test 8 A USE OF ENGLISH

A Complete the sentences with relative pronouns *who/that/which/where/whose* or ✗ if the pronoun is not necessary.   (3 points)

0 I have a new skirt _____**✗**_____ I really like.

1 John, _____ mother is a painter, is my best friend.

2 We went to Mechanicsburg, _____ my grandparents live.

3 There are some boys in my class _____ play basketball very well.

4 I loved the book _____ you gave me for my birthday.

5 Frank has a small cottage _____ is not very far from Warsaw.

6 I don't watch films _____ make me cry.

B Use the prepositions from the box to complete the text. Some are used more than once.   (4 points)

between, near, in, on, at, during

As a senior lawyer I work (0) _____**between**_____ twelve and fourteen hours a day and usually come back home (1) _____ 9 p.m. My wife complains that I don't spend enough time with her. We can do something together only (2) _____ Sundays and then we usually go to the restaurant (3) _____ our house. When I have several days off, for example (4) _____ Christmas, we try to go out of London. Last year (5) _____ December we went to Brighton to visit my mother. She was born (6) _____ December 25, so we celebrated her birthday (7) _____ our visit. My mum's life was completely different from mine. She could always find a good balance (8) _____ her work and family life.

C Complete the second sentences so that they have the same meaning as the first.   (5 points)

0 'Stop making noise,' said the grandmother to her grandson.

The grandmother _ordered her grandson to stop_
_making noise_____ .

1 'Don't drink or eat anything in the reading room, please,' the librarian said to Chris.

The librarian _____

_____ in the reading room.

2 My grandma asked me to help her with the housework.

'_____

with the housework, please?' my grandma asked me.

3 'You should drink a glass of water and lie down for a while,' I said to my younger sister.

I _____ .

_____ for a while.

4 My parents often tell me not to let strangers into the house.

'_____

_____,' my parents often say to me.

5 'Tidy up your room before going to the cinema,' my mother said to me.

My mother _____

_____ before going to the cinema.

D Put the words and phrases from the box under the correct headings.   (5 points)

stone, geometric, dark, concrete, light, wood, bright, brick, round, square

SHAPES:

_____

MATERIALS:

_____

COLOURS:

_____

E Match the multi-part verbs with their definitions.   (3 points)

0 run out of	a) to get close
1 fall in love	b) to become free of something/somebody
2 get rid of	c) to pass
3 make up for	d) to see in many directions
4 look around	e) to start to love
5 come near	f) to have no more of something
6 go by	g) to compensate

0	1	2	3	4	5	6
f						

Total **20**

Test 8 B USE OF ENGLISH

A Complete the sentences with relative pronouns *who/that/which/where/whose* **or** *X* **if the pronoun is not necessary.** (3 points)

0 I have a new skirt _____*X*_____ I really like.

1 I know many people in Finland _____ speak excellent English.

2 I never go to shops _____ the prices are too high.

3 There aren't any restaurants _____ serve good food in this city.

4 My sister has a boyfriend _____ cat doesn't drink milk at all.

5 Some people _____ I know go to church every Sunday.

6 I like boys _____ are handsome and have a good sense of humour.

B Use the prepositions from the box to complete the text. Some are used more than once. (4 points)

across, at, between, during, in, near, on

I come from Brighton but (0) _____*in*_____ the spring of 1995 I moved out and now I live with my wife and children (1) _____ London. Our life here is much faster than before. I usually get up (2) _____ 6.00 a.m., have a quick breakfast and rush to work. Fortunately, my office is (3) _____ our flat so I just need to drive (4) _____ the bridge to get to work. (5) _____ the morning it takes me (6) _____ ten and fifteen minutes to get to the office. I usually work for about nine hours and (7) _____ this time I rarely find a moment to eat lunch. It is even worse (8) _____ Mondays when we have weekly meetings.

C Complete the second sentences so that they have the same meaning as the first. (5 points)

0 'Stop making noise,' said the grandmother to her grandson.

The grandmother *ordered her grandson to stop*

making noise .

1 Tom asked me to lend him some money till tomorrow.

'_____ till tomorrow, please?' Tom asked me.

2 'Think twice before you make a decision,' my father often says to me.

My father often _____

_____ make a decision.

3 We told Barbara not to bring any sweets for our children.

'_____ , please,' we said to Barbara.

4 'I think you should go to the dentist,' I said to my mother.

I _____

_____ to the dentist.

5 'Don't use your mobile phone during the landing, please,' the flight attendant said to Tom.

The flight attendant _____

_____ during the landing.

D Put the words and phrases from the box under the correct headings. (5 points)

clear, zoom lens, castle, straight, office block, camera, strong, flash, tripod, museum

KINDS OF BUILDINGS:

_____ .

LINES:

_____ .

PHOTOGRAPHY EQUIPMENT:

_____ .

E Match the multi-part verbs with their definitions. (3 points)

0 run out of	a) to return
1 get back	b) to compensate for something
2 think about	c) to appear, to be seen or heard
3 get near to	d) to become close to someone
4 make up for	e) to pass
5 go by	f) to have no more of something
6 come out	g) to consider

0	1	2	3	4	5	6
f						

Total | **20**

Test 8 READING

Read the text and decide if the statements are true (T) or false (F).

1. ☐ Astronauts can see the Great Wall of China from space.
2. ☐ The Great Wall of China was designed to look like a snake.
3. ☐ The Great Wall of China was built of one type of material.
4. ☐ Prisoners and criminals were not allowed to build the Wall.
5. ☐ The builders of the Great Wall of China wore poor clothes.
6. ☐ The builders of the Great Wall of China had enough food to live.
7. ☐ The Wall's towers are over two hundred metres from each other.
8. ☐ In the towers of the Great Wall there lived about one million slaves.

The Great Wall of China

The Great Wall of China is the only man-made construction that can be seen from space. It is 6,000 kilometres long. It runs along China's northern border and has an unusual shape. It looks as if its architects did not have any specific plans. It looks like a snake or a long road. Nobody knows why its shape is like this but legend states that it was built to imitate the movements of a dragon – a popular religious symbol in China.

The section of the Wall visited by most tourists is at Badaling Pass near Peking. Here, the building material is grey granite blocks, 6 metres high. On both sides of its roof, there are low walls which protect you from falling off the Wall. In the middle, there is a road which is wide enough for five horses running side by side. Other sections of the Great Wall are built of various materials, often of poor quality, for example of wood or sand depending on whether the wall crossed deserts, plains or the country.

The people who were forced to build the Great Wall were often those who could not pay their taxes, prisoners of war and criminals. There were about one million slaves working on the wall. They lived in poor conditions, in places called work camps. They worked without clothes during the summer and they wore only animal skins in the winter. They often died of disease and hunger. Those who died were often buried in its foundations, making the Wall the 'world's longest cemetery'.

There are still many of the original 25,000 towers left. They are about 12 metres high and the distance between two neighbouring towers is over 200 metres. The army usually lived in these towers. In the period of the Wall's glory almost a million men stayed there.

Today the Great Wall is one of China's tourist attractions. Where else in the world can you see something built by man over twenty-two centuries ago?

Total | 8

Test 8 WRITING

You have just moved to a flat but you are not pleased with it. Write a letter to the landlord (about 100–150 words) and:

- say what you are not happy with;
- how it interferes with your studying;
- ask for help to solve the problem;
- express your hope that it is going to improve.

Total | 20

Test D LISTENING

Harry and his father are talking about ancient civilisations. Listen to their conversation and circle the correct answer, a, b or c.

1 The Incas used _____ to build their cities.
   a wood
   b stone
   c iron

2 The Incas built
   a castles and palaces.
   b structures in a shape of the sun, moon and stars.
   c fortresses and pyramids.

3 The most popular designs that the Inca architects made were
   a the symbols of the sun, moon and stars.
   b the figures of animals, birds and insects.
   c the round patterns in a shape of a wheel.

4 To build their stone cities, the Incas used
   a tools which our civilisation does not know.
   b iron tools.
   c animals.

5 The Inca empire had a great influence on
   a today's architecture.
   b people's beliefs.
   c people's contact with UFOs.

6 In Peru the Incas made
   a their largest stone city.
   b a massive iron structure.
   c big geometric signs.

Total | 6

Test D SPEAKING

Student A
Look at the photograph and answer the questions.

1 Are the people in the picture enjoying themselves? Why do you think so?
2 What is your favourite way of spending free time?

Total | 20

Student B
Look at the photograph and answer the questions.

1 Is the man in the picture painting for pleasure? Why do you think so?
2 What is your favourite painting? Why?

Total | 20

Test D READING

Read the story of The Beatles and decide if the sentences are true (T) or false (F).

1 ☐ The Beatles recorded together until 1970.
2 ☐ The three Beatles wanted to record only their old hits.
3 ☐ In 1994 the programme about The Beatles was going to be shown on TV.
4 ☐ The new book was going to appear in bookshops.
5 ☐ Only their old fans were interested in the special TV programme.
6 ☐ Not many people expected to see The Beatles in concert again.

The Beatles are back?

At the start of the year 1994, the world received a shocking piece of news: '*The Beatles are to record again for the first time in 24 years.*' The band's three remaining members at that time, Paul McCartney, George Harrison and Ringo Starr (without John Lennon who was murdered in 1980) announced plans to record together.

The three musicians did not want to record only new versions of their old songs. They were also interested in recording new music. They were going to make a ten-hour special video-biography to be shown on British television later that year. The new project would include a lot of unpublished documentaries, interviews and materials from The Beatles' private collections. At the same time a new book about the group was going to appear in the bookshops. The fans would also have the chance to buy recordings of their live concerts on five CDs in the music shops.

Fans of the famous four were hoping that this comeback would not run into any difficulties. In the earlier years, The Beatles had a long history of arguments over money and copyright. This was one of the reasons why the band decided to stop working together ten years before Lennon's death.

Now that they were returning to the stage, The Beatles' old and new fans expected a new kind of fascination and excitement. They were hoping that their idols would remind them of the good old days of rock and roll. Actually, many of them never thought that one day they would get yet another chance to watch their idols perform again.

Total	6

Test D WRITING

Write a four-paragraph description (about 100–150 words) of a building you saw on holiday. Choose from the following options:

a castle   a palace   a skyscraper   a church   a museum

Describe the following features:

- the building's name and location;
- style/period it was built in;
- materials used to build it;
- features on the outside and inside;
- furniture and decorations;
- people who lived there;
- events that took place there;
- recommendations.

Total	20

Final Test A USE OF ENGLISH

A There is a mistake in each line of this text. Find it and correct it as in the example. (10 points)

0   I'm not sure why, but (I have never liked) reading

_____ I never liked _____

1   when I was younger. I always found more nice

_____

2   things to do. I spent too many of my free time

_____

3   drawing or playing with dolls. Reading the books

_____

4   was the worst activity for me. I often didn't make

_____

5   my homework if the teacher asks us to read a book.

_____

6   My mother thought I just needed any help and

_____

7   more patience, but she's been wrong. Fortunately,

_____

8   I was good at a history and even better at

_____

9   maths. I hope my son is going to like reading.

_____

10 But if he will not, I will not worry about it.

_____

B Put the verbs in brackets in the right form. (6 points)

0   My grandmother _____gave_____ (give) me this ring ten years ago.

1   They are very angry because they _____ (lose) three games.

2   I'm afraid she can't come to the phone now. She _____ (take) a shower.

3   English _____ (speak) all over the world.

4   There are no clouds in the sky; it _____ (not rain).

5   Susan Vega _____ (give) a lot of flowers after her concert in Paris.

6   I'm sure they would offer me a job if I _____ (know) two foreign languages.

C Circle the correct alternative in each sentence. (3 points)

0   Do you ever feel (bored)/boring at the opera?

1   You *mustn't/don't have to* do it today. We will have plenty of time tomorrow.

2   There are only two good football players for me, one is Pele and *the other/the second* Maradona.

3   The film wasn't very interesting, *was/did* it?

4   Our new music teacher is very gifted. He plays *violin/the violin* very well.

5   She usually goes to the cinema alone. I guess, she doesn't have *no/any* close friends.

6   I don't like meeting people *whose/which* main hobby is work and earning money.

D Use the prepositions from the box to complete the sentences. Some are used more than once. (3 points)

at, to, into, of, for

0   It's funny but my twenty-five-year-old brother is still afraid _____of_____ darkness.

1   Have you already seen this exhibition _____ the Centre for Medieval Art?

2   You are eighteen years old and from now on you're responsible _____ yourself.

3   Alice is very careful with money. She always puts some _____ her bank account.

4   I was really proud _____ myself when I finally passed my driving test.

5   Your essay is very similar _____ his. Have you copied it from him?

6   Cambridge is famous _____ its university and academic life.

E Complete the sentences with one word in each gap. (5 points)

0   I try to _____write_____ down everything the teacher says.

1   Smoking is very bad for you. I honestly feel you should _____ it up.

2   When the temperature went _____ to −20°C, we decided to go back.

3   George went to live with his aunt, but after two years she decided to _____ him back to his parents.

4 I've never got _____ with my boss. We have completely different personalities.

5 Although after the accident Joan can't move very quickly, she is determined to _____ on working.

F **Match the words from the two columns to form compound words.** (5 points)

0	natural	a)	camera
1	equal	b)	meat
2	tough	c)	roof
3	detached	d)	disaster
4	tinned	e)	line
5	digital	f)	voice
6	fishing	g)	place
7	distorted	h)	rights
8	straight	i)	food
9	sheltered	j)	boat
10	curved	k)	house

0	1	2	3	4	5	6	7	8	9	10
d										

G **Write the words or expressions from the box under the correct headings. Then add three more words or expressions to each list.** (8 points)

crime, pleased, French windows, breeze

WEATHER:

_____

FEELINGS:

_____

URBAN PROBLEMS:

_____

IN THE HOUSE:

_____

Total		40

Final Test B USE OF ENGLISH

A There is a mistake in each line of this text. Find it and correct it as in the example. (10 points)

0   I love watching TV late (in night.) My parents

_____at night_____

1   usually don't let me staying up so late during

_____

2   a week, but I can do it on Friday or Saturday.

_____

3   My father and brother, which are great sports

_____

4   fans, always want to watch a football matches.

_____

5   Fortunately, none of them quickly fall asleep

_____

6   and I can choose programmes whose are

_____

7   interesting for me. Next week I watch a comedy

_____

8   with Dustin Hoffman and any other good actors.

_____

9   The film is not very long, but it is starting late.

_____

10 I hope I will not fall asleep before it will end.

_____

B Put the verbs in brackets in the right form. (6 points)

0   My grandmother _____gave_____ (give) me this ring ten years ago.

1   My sister _____ (offer) a very good job last year.

2   There is a lot of glass on the floor. Who _____ (break) the window?

3   I _____ (write) the essay when you called me yesterday.

4   We _____ (not see) each other before.

5   She won't talk to you if you _____ (not apologise) for your behaviour.

6   I'm afraid credit cards _____ (not accept) here.

C Circle the correct alternative in each sentence. (3 points)

0   Do you ever feel (bored)/boring at the opera?

1   You are very keen on classical music, *aren't/don't* you?

2   Girls, when I am not here you *mustn't/don't have to* touch the oven. Is that clear?

3   This Ford is *more/the most* comfortable car I have ever had.

4   I work very *hard/hardly* for my money, so don't tell me what I should spend it on.

5   Most of my classmates study on weekdays, so we usually go out at *weekend/the weekend*.

6   How *much/many* did you have to pay for the telephone bill last month?

D Use the prepositions from the box to complete the sentences. Some are used more than once. (3 points)

about, on, from, of, for

0   It's funny but my twenty-five-year-old brother is still afraid _____*of*_____ the dark.

1   I asked _____ a discount when I noticed a small stain on the blouse.

2   They are twins but in personality they seem very different _____ each other.

3   She was born _____ March 1. Is her zodiac sign Pisces?

4   John wanted me to take care _____ his dog while he was away on holiday.

5   She avoids you because she is tired _____ listening about your problems.

6   Oh, come on! Stop complaining _____ everything and do something!

E Complete the sentences with one word in each gap. (5 points)

0   I try to _____write_____ down everything the teacher says.

1   My daughter is a very good girl. She has given _____ all her old toys to poor children.

2   My younger brother drives me crazy! He always _____ over to another channel without asking permission.

3   Food is very expensive in this country. The prices have gone _____ again!

4   He emigrated to Canada to _____ away from poverty and unemployment in his homeland.

5   Let me know if you _____ across my ball-point pen. I think I've left it at your place.

F **Match the words from the two columns to form compound words.**   (5 points)

0	washing	a)	ceremony
1	hunger	b)	fighter
2	child	c)	skiing
3	wedding	d)	machine
4	savings	e)	level
5	food	f)	strike
6	search	g)	account
7	downhill	h)	mixer
8	drug	i)	labour
9	sea	j)	addiction
10	fire	k)	engine

0	1	2	3	4	5	6	7	8	9	10
d										

G **Write the words or expressions from the box under the correct headings. Then add three more words or expressions to each list.**   (8 points)

tripod, famine, reality show, generous

PERSONALITY:

_____

PHOTOGRAPHY:

_____

NATURAL DISASTERS:

_____

TV PROGRAMMES:

_____

Total | 40 |

Final Test LISTENING

Listen to the interview with a Polish singer and decide if the sentences are true (T) or false (F).

1 ☐ Kasia sings about love, anger and fear.

2 ☐ All of her songs are in English.

3 ☐ She prefers to sing in English because it sounds better.

4 ☐ Sting congratulated Kasia on her performance before his concert.

5 ☐ Kasia has got two children.

6 ☐ Kasia has written a lullaby for her son.

Total	6

Final Test SPEAKING

You are organising an end-of-school event. Student A wants to perform a play and Student B wants to invite a music band. Give a short presentation about your choice to persuade your teacher.

Student A	*Student B*
• give the name of the play and who wrote it • explain what the play is about • give reasons why you think it's a good choice • compare your idea with inviting a music band and point out differences • say what you need to put the play on stage	• give the name of the band • explain what kind of music they are playing • give reasons why you think it's a good choice • compare your idea with performing a play and point out differences • say what you need to invite the band

Total	20		Total	20

Final Test WRITING

Choose one option from the list of seaside attractions and write a report (about 100–150 words) describing its good and bad points. Decide who is going to read your report.

A   a seaside hotel
B   a cruise around the island
C   a local underwater sealife observatory

Divide your text into four paragraphs. Write:

- who you are;
- who the report is to;
- general description of the activity;

- good points;
- bad points;
- your recommendations.

Useful linking words:
on the one hand, on the other hand, however, but, not only ... but also, either, in addition, too, etc.

Total	20

Final Test READING

Read the text and decide if the statements are true (T) or false (F).

1 ☐ Bodiam Castle was built in the late fourteenth century.

2 ☐ Bodiam Castle's first owner was a knight.

3 ☐ There was water around the castle.

4 ☐ There was one large kitchen in the castle.

5 ☐ Although the castle was a lord's residence, it was never peaceful.

6 ☐ Lord Curzon gave Bodiam Castle to the National Trust.

Bodiam Castle

If you go sightseeing in the south of England, you must not miss one of the most beautiful medieval castles ever built – Bodiam Castle. Bodiam is everyone's fairy-tale castle. Although time and man's hand have ruined the inside, its outer walls and towers stand as they did when completed in 1388. Like many medieval castles, Bodiam was both the fortress and residence of a lord – in this case Sir Edward Dalyngrigge, a knight.

Sir Edward's castle was designed in the most up-to-date style. Its layout was simple but effective. It had a rectangular shape and there was a tower at each of the four corners. It was surrounded by a moat, a deep pool filled with water protecting the castle from attackers. The trees around the moat had to be cut up to avoid giving cover to an attacker. The only way leading inside the castle was through a wooden bridge over the moat.

Bodiam Castle looked splendid. Its size was impressive. It was probably one of the largest buildings in Sussex in the late fourteenth century. Perhaps as many as one thousand men worked on its construction and they came from all over England. They designed and built Bodiam's rooms, halls, chapels and many kitchens which are now open to the public.

Bodiam was home to many residents over the years. Although built for war, life there was usually peaceful because Bodiam was never attacked. It was captured twice without resistance, in both cases by other Englishmen. In 1916 it was purchased by Lord Curzon, who took good care of its ruins, carrying out the most necessary repairs. In 1925, he asked the National Trust to look after the castle and its beautiful countryside.

Total	6

Tapescripts

Test 1 LISTENING

Hatton Hotels

Are you tired of the noise and rush of city life? Do you feel like spending your free time close to nature? Stay at one of our Hatton Hotels, offering you fantastic weekends away all over the country.

Hatton Hotels' tradition of good service and value for money means that at any one of over forty Hatton Hotels there is a warm welcome waiting for you. So, if you are looking for a relaxing break, you are sure to find a Hatton Hotel to suit your needs.

We are famous for our tradition of fine food, comfort and hospitality. At every Hatton Hotel there is a modern Hatton Restaurant offering a range of classic steaks, salads, fish and vegetarian dishes. There is also an attractive Cocktail Bar which provides a fine selection of light meals and drinks. Both are wonderful places to relax in a friendly atmosphere. All our bedrooms are large, comfortable and have all the necessary facilities, including a private bathroom, cable television and a direct-line telephone.

Almost all Hatton Hotels are perfectly situated for visiting many of the local attractions like old churches, castles, and other historic places of interest. For those who choose to stay with us at weekends, we have a special offer – a free four-hour tour of the surrounding area. And for those who want to remember their stay at our hotels we have a special souvenir when they leave.

If you are interested in joining us at one of our Hatton Hotels, simply pick up a WEEKENDS AWAY brochure at any Hatton Hotel or call our free line 0 800 768 563.

Hatton Weekends Away – a great tradition and excellent value for money.

Test A LISTENING

Mickey Mouse – a cartoon hero

What is a cartoon? It's a film that tells a story by using moving drawings instead of real people and places. Cartoons are usually amusing. The funniest cartoon characters in children's movies are animals which behave like people and have many crazy ideas which make us laugh.

Cinema's first cartoon character was Gertie the Dinosaur. She first appeared on the screen in 1909. Since then, a long list of cartoon stars have followed Gertie into the movies.

The greatest cartoon-maker in cinema history was Walt Disney, who has often been quoted as saying, 'It all started with a mouse.' It's true. Mickey Mouse has become an international cartoon superstar. Without him, Disney could not have made his own dreams come true.

Many artists worked on Mickey's appearance and personality because Disney couldn't draw Mickey Mouse himself. They tried hard to make Mickey look angry, sad, scared or happy. They changed his body a few times until they found the ideal shape for his head, body and ears. Until 1946, Walt Disney provided Mickey's voice himself.

Disney produced his first black and white Mickey Mouse cartoon in 1928. It was a great hit with both children and adults. Since then, Mickey has starred in about 120 cartoons – often joined by the four famous characters: Donald Duck, Minnie, Goofy and Pluto. They have made Mickey's adventures more colourful and amusing. They have also become children's favourite cartoon characters all over the world and 'Disney' is still the best-loved name in children's entertainment.

Test 3 LISTENING

Thanksgiving Day

Jim Morrow, Interviewer (JM): Welcome, everybody. This is Jim Morrow and your favourite programme 'CELEBRATIONS OF THE YEAR'. Today, our guest Tom Tripleton, who comes from the United States of America, is going to tell us about his favourite holiday – Thanksgiving Day. Well, Tom, what is Thanksgiving Day?

Tom Tripleton (TT): Thank you, Jim. I'd say that after Christmas, Thanksgiving Day is the second most important family occasion in the United States. We celebrate it every year, on the fourth Thursday in November.

(JM): What exactly do you celebrate?

(TT): We celebrate the good fortune of the early colonists who arrived in America in 1620 in what is now Plymouth, Massachusetts.

(JM): You say – good fortune?

(TT): Well, at first, the early English settlers had many problems like poor health and sickness. However, they gradually learnt to live in their new world and built settlements. You know, they had to cut down the trees in the forests to build their houses and create fields, which was very tiring. Fortunately, later, friendly Indians taught them how to hunt, fish and grow crops in their fields.

(JM): They were lucky, weren't they?

(TT): That's right. When they collected their crops in the autumn, they were very happy because they knew they had enough food for the winter ahead. So they decided to have a feast to thank God for their good luck. They invited their helpful Indian neighbours and celebrated for several days.

(JM): So what happens today in America?

(TT): Today, American families meet on Thanksgiving Day and prepare a traditional Thanksgiving dinner.

We have roast turkey, sweet potatoes and sweet corn. In large cities, big department stores sponsor Thanksgiving Day parades. They introduce the Christmas shopping season.

(JM): Do children like this holiday?

(TT): Oh, yes, they love it. The holiday is always on Thursday, so they get a long four-day weekend.

(JM): The Thanksgiving holiday, isn't it wonderful? Tom, thank you very much.

(TT): My pleasure.

Test B LISTENING

The history of money

Can you imagine the world without money? It is quite impossible. Money – they say – makes the world go round. Why is that so? Well, think of all the situations in which you have to pay for the things you buy – like food, clothes, medicine, newspapers, or for the services you get, like a new hairstyle or car repairs. Think of the entertainment you have to pay for – tickets to concerts, sports matches, favourite books, CDs and holidays. You can have it all if you've got the money.

Money has played an important role in every civilisation.

It has taken various forms and has changed many times over the centuries. The first form of payment was the exchange of goods. People usually exchanged animal skins and meat, fruit and vegetables, cloth and precious stones. In ancient Egypt they used metal bars which were cut into smaller parts if necessary. In the seventh century BC the first coins appeared. They were usually made of silver or gold and their value depended on the amount of metal in each coin. With time, coins became very popular and many countries produced their own currency.

The introduction of paper money – banknotes – in the seventeenth century was the beginning of banking systems in many European countries. Since then, banks have offered a wide range of services like loans, bank accounts, etc. Today, people pay for things in different ways: they pay in cash, by cheque or by credit card. The last one, it seems, is the most convenient form of payment. Many people believe that one day money in the form of coins, banknotes, cheques and magnetic cards will totally disappear and that all buying and selling will be done via the Internet.

Mid-year Test LISTENING

Driving cars in England

It is the same to drive a car in England as any other country. To change a car wheel in the wind and rain is as pleasant outside London as outside Rio de Janeiro. If your car stops moving anywhere – in Sydney or in Edinburgh – you will still have to push it. But the English car driver is different from the European car driver so there are some things you must remember when you drive in England. Let me give you three examples.

One. In English towns you must drive at thirty miles per hour. The police watch carefully for drivers who go too fast. It is difficult to know if a police car is following you but if you are intelligent and have very good eyes, you will see these cars. Remember: the police usually drive white cars, two policemen sit in each car and you can read the word POLICE in large letters on the front and back of these cars.

Two. England is the only country in the world where you must leave your car lights on when you park your car at night in a busy street with lots of street lights. When you come back to the car, you cannot start it again. The car will not work; it's dead. But it is wonderful! There are fewer cars on the road and the number of road crashes goes down. This makes driving on roads safe.

And three. If you park your car in the City or the West End of London, two or three policemen will run up and tell you 'You cannot park here! Move along!' So where can you park? The policemen don't know. But, they are right. Cars need to move, and move fast, not stop and make life difficult for people in the street.

Test 5 LISTENING

Computers in education

Interviewer (I): Susan, how long have you been a teacher?

Susan (S): Er ... for about ten years.

(I): What do you think about the role of computers in education?

(S): Well, recently, computers have become a very helpful teaching aid in the classroom. More schools provide their learners with opportunities to use computer technology (the Internet in particular) to learn new and interesting information. I think it's useful not only for the teaching of subjects like physics, maths, chemistry, biology and geography, but also for practising foreign languages, especially English.

(I): Why do you think teachers should use computers in the English language classroom?

(S): That's an interesting question. First of all, most of the material on the Internet is in English. Students can see examples of real-life communication, find out about the use of the grammar and vocabulary they are learning in their lessons and find all sorts of online publications in a quick and convenient way. Secondly, students can expand their horizons by getting to know a lot about people and far away places they will never be able to visit. They can read texts on the websites, play videos, solve quizzes and join discussion groups. These are only some of the options available to students. Additionally, they can become pen friends or rather email friends and exchange personal information over the Internet.

(I): And how can the Internet be useful for the teachers?

(S): Oh, the Internet gives teachers many ideas for making their lessons attractive. It has popular dictionary sites, pages with information about English-speaking countries, lesson plans and attractive collections of exercises written by experienced teachers from various parts of the world.

(I): In other words, it helps teachers to make their lessons more challenging and interesting for students.

(S): That's true. It is not very difficult to make students use the computers for learning purposes. I believe most students would love the chance of having at least one lesson a week to surf the Internet.

Test C LISTENING

Where the River Jordan ends

The Dead Sea is situated where the River Jordan ends, just 24 kilometres east of Jerusalem. It is really a lake. It extends for about 74 kilometres and is 16 kilometres wide so it is quite small but it is extremely deep – about 300 metres.

Originally, the Dead Sea was about the same size as today. Then the climate of the area changed and became wetter. This change caused the Dead Sea to grow longer. However, after some time, the climate changed again and the lake returned to its original size and shape.

The Dead Sea is one of the saltiest lakes in the world. One litre of sea water may contain up to 327 grams of salt. With so much salt in the water, no fish or flora can live in the Dead Sea. However, for people who love swimming, it's the ideal place to relax. And the salt in the water makes it easy to swim without any effort at all!

There is not much rain in the area of the Dead Sea. It usually rains only between October and March. The temperatures are different depending on the area. In the northern parts of the Dead Sea in January it can be only 14 degrees centigrade; however, in August in the south it can get up to 34 degrees. The highest recorded temperature for this region is 51 degrees centigrade.

Nearly twenty years ago there was a plan to build a canal between the Dead Sea and the Mediterranean. This would make the level of the water in the Dead Sea go up. However, the cost of doing this is so enormous that the project cannot go ahead yet. So, at the moment nothing is being done.

Test 7 LISTENING

Rik Palieri

Interviewer (I): Rik, at the age of fifteen, like many teenagers, you were attracted to rock music.

Rik Palieri (RP): Yes, that's correct. Actually, I was even working for a rock band, carrying their instruments.

(I): Really? Did you play any musical instrument at that time? A guitar perhaps?

(RP): Yes, but it wasn't a guitar. The first instrument I

learnt to play was a banjo. I practised playing it a lot. One day, however, I saw a photo of Polish bagpipes in *National Geographic* and I decided I had to get some for myself.

(I): Well, so, what happened then?

(RP): In 1980, I went to Poland because I was invited to a folk festival. There I saw and heard a real kobza, (the Polish name for bagpipes). I fell in love with it immediately. I spent six months studying, learning to play this instrument although it was extremely difficult. Do you know that I even learnt to speak Polish?

(I): Did you like it there?

(RP): Of course. Especially the folk costumes and traditions of the mountains. I even took a Polish sheep dog back home to America.

(I): So, what is your life like now?

(RP): Now, I am thirty-eight. I am a folk singer, composer and story-teller. I regularly give concerts at festivals, in clubs, pubs and schools. I sing ballads, blues, country and Polish folk songs. I have performed in Italy, France, Great Britain and Poland.

(I): Do you travel to Poland sometimes?

(RP): Quite often, I must say. To look for inspiration, traditions and real folklore.

(I): Rik, is there anything you would like to tell your fans?

(RP): Oh, yes. Never forget about where you come from. Always remember your country's traditions. Otherwise, if you lose your folklore, you lose a part of yourselves.

(I): Thank you, Rik.

Test D LISTENING

The Inca empire

Harry (H): Dad, I need your help. I have to prepare a speech about an ancient civilisation for my history class. I don't know what to choose.

Dad (D): How about the Roman empire?

(H): No, we've already done it. I'd like to talk about something special.

(D): Perhaps the Incas then ...

(H): That sounds better. But I don't know much about their civilisation.

(D): I'll tell you what I know so you can decide if it is interesting enough.

(H): Great!

(D): Well, first of all, the Incas were famous for their magnificent architecture. For hundreds of years, the cities and towns that they built were forgotten, but today, you can still admire their ruins. They tell you a lot about the Inca world of the past.

(H): What is so exciting about these cities?

(D): The Incas built huge fortresses, gigantic pyramids, and so called stone cities. Their architects often designed various geometric patterns and figures of birds, animals and insects. We do not know how the Incas built these massive structures. They did not have wheels or iron tools and they did not use animals. But still, the buildings were perfectly designed and every stone fitted into its place perfectly. Do you know that some of the Incas' structures and patterns have been discovered by accident?

(H): (surprised) Really? What made the Inca empire disappear?

(D): I'm not sure. But it is interesting how they have influenced the beliefs of people of various nationalities and religions all over the world. There are the huge geometric designs in the fields near Peru's southern coast. They show some sea animals but they are so big you can recognise them only from an aeroplane. Many people who believe in UFOs believe that the Incas made these signs to help spaceships find a place to land. Others believe that these drawings or images showed different positions of the sun, moon and stars at important times of the year.

(H): It really is unusual.

(D): Now Harry, get that book about the Inca cities. It's over there. You will find a lot of information about life on the South American Continent 500 years ago.

(H): Thanks, Dad.

Final Test LISTENING

Kasia

Interviewer (I): Kasia, you are one of the best Polish female vocalists. What do you think makes your songs so well received?

Kasia (K): Well, I think it's not only the sound of each song but most of all my lyrics are really emotional. I like to tell people what I feel. Sometimes these are bitter feelings – you can be rich and have good looks but that doesn't necessarily mean that you are happy. You have to look for happiness inside yourself.

(I): Are all your songs about love?

(K): Not all. Some of them are love songs, but I also sing about anger, fear and other human emotions.

(I): Some of your songs are in English, aren't they?

(K): Yes, I sing a lot in English. I used to think that you can't possibly sing well in Polish. English simply sounds better. But, on the other hand, people would like to understand what I'm singing. Now that many people know English they understand the English lyrics as well.

(I): Kasia, do you ever feel stage fright?

(K): I've felt stage fright a lot of times, for example, when I was performing as a supporting artist before Sting's concert in Warsaw. His shows usually gather a very demanding audience. But it worked, I got applause from his band, and the master himself came up to me to shake my hand as if to show that he was impressed.

(I): Apart from being an artist, you are a mother, too. Have you ever written a song for your daughter?

(K): Oh, yes. One of my albums features a lullaby dedicated to her. It says, 'You are this tiny bit of happiness that turns each day into a holiday.'

(I): Your fans love you, and they say that they dream of meeting you in person one day.

(K): Perhaps it will come true, then.

(I): Thank you, Kasia.

(K): Thank you.

Key

Use of English

Test 1 A

A: (1 point each) 1 is having; 2 have; 3 don't believe; 4 isn't writing; 5 are watching

B: (1 point each) 1 has drunk it; 2 haven't cleaned it; 3 has lost it; 4 have fed them

C: (0.5 point each) 1 at; 2 for; 3 in; 4 of

D: (0.5 point each) go jogging; do the housework, a lot of exercise; make plans, a noise, the beds

E: (1 point each) 1 pleased; 2 bungalow; 3 lay; 4 wardrobe; 5 pass; 6 worried

Test 1 B

A: (1 point each) 1 are showing; 2 doesn't love; 3 are working; 4 thinks; 5 am studying

B: (1 point each) 1 has broken it; 2 have spent it; 3 has eaten it; 4 haven't painted them

C: (0.5 point each) 1 in; 2 at; 3 of; 4 with

D: (0.5 point each) make a mistake, a phone call; have a shower, an argument; do repairs, the cooking

E: (1 point each) 1 creative; 2 semi-detached; 3 tidy; 4 dishwasher; 5 grow; 6 angry

Test 2 A

A: (0.5 point each) 1 was driving; 2 yet; 3 a bath; 4 haven't seen; 5 began; 6 played; 7 train; 8 has he won; 9 the theatre; 10 did your sister do

B (1 point each) 1 was; 2 was sitting; 3 came up; 4 spoke; 5 fell; 6 had; 7 has visited

C: (0.5 point each) 1 independence; 2 succeed; 3 painful; 4 inability; 5 indecisive; 6 dead; 7 anger; 8 suspicious

D: (0.5 point each) 1 boring; 2 sensitive; 3 generous; 4 calm; 5 cruel; 6 overrated; 7 kind; 8 skilful

Test 2 B

A: (0.5 point each) 1 won; 2 the piano; 3 have you travelled; 4 the cinema; 5 did you do; 6 German; 7 was reading; 8 yet; 9 haven't ridden; 10 called

B: (1 point each) 1 was talking; 2 was reading; 3 heard; 4 liked; 5 began; 6 went; 7 has come back

C: (0.5 point each) 1 freedom; 2 poisonous; 3 hatred; 4 dishonest; 5 activities; 6 alive; 7 enable; 8 unsuccessful

D: (0.5 point each) 1 violent; 2 brilliant; 3 decisive; 4 brave; 5 awful; 6 hard-working; 7 wise; 8 arrogant

Test 3 A

A: (0.5 point each) 1 mustn't; 2 don't have to; 3 can; 4 must; 5 can't; 6 mustn't; 7 have to; 8 don't have to

B: (0.5 point each) 1 better; 2 the tallest; 3 the most intelligent; 4 less interesting; 5 the worst; 6 the laziest; 7 cleverer; 8 younger; 9 the kindest; 10 easier

C: (0.5 point each) 1 fashionable Italian leather; beautiful short dark brown; 3 horrible bright red wollen; 4 young British

D: (0.5 point each) 1 f; 2 c; 3 a; 4 h; 5 e; 6 g; 7 i; 8 b

E: (1 point each) 1 put; 2 excursion/trip; 3 together; 4 bride; 5 victory

Test 3 B

A: (0.5 point each) 1 can; 2 have to; 3 can't; 4 must; 5 can; 6 don't have to; 7 mustn't; 8 don't have to

B: (0.5 point each) 1 the oldest; 2 the tallest; 3 the most intelligent; 4 less clever; 5 worse; 6 lazier; 7 more attractive; 8 the most boring; 9 the best; 10 more helpful

C: (0.5 point each) 1 old-fashioned dark wollen; 2 beautiful big blue; 3 cheap nylon; 4 comfortable small German

D: (0.5 point each) 1 b; 2 g; 3 a; 4 i; 5 e; 6 c; 7 f; 8 h

E: (1 point each) 1 up; 2 bridegroom/groom; 3 get; 4 uniform; 5 award

Test 4 A

A: (0.5 point each) 1 will; 2 Are you going to; 3 is not going to; 4 will; 5 am going to; 6 will

B: (0.5 point each) 1 some; 2 much; 3 no; 4 any; 5 much; 6 no, many; 7 any

C: (1 point each) 1 there isn't enough money; 2 to my other one; 3 All of them .../ problems with their two children; 4 There are a few eggs ...; 5 helps other people

D: (0.5 point each) 1 fascinating; 2 depressed; 3 worried; 4 relaxing

E: (1 point each) 1 earn; 2 hairdryer; 3 save; 4 easy; 5 away; 6 lend

Test 4 B

A: (0.5 point each) 1 are going to; 2 will; 3 is going to; 4 will; 5 will; 6 is going to

B: (0.5 point each) 1 some; 2 any; 3 much; 4 some; 5 any, many; 6 no; 7 much

C: (1 point each) 1 There aren't many people ...; 2 the other one; 3 none of us; 4 I have a little time; 5 Both of us ...

D: (0.5 point each) 1 interested; 2 bored; 3 amazing; 4 excited

E: (1 point each) 1 borrow; 2 vacuum; 3 discount; 4 reliable; 5 into; 6 note

Test 5 A

A: (1 point each) 1 would visit; 2 has; 3 would go; 4 boils; 5 knew; 6 ask; 7 didn't come; 8 don't water

B: (0.5 point each) 1 My grandma normally walks very slowly; 2 Fiona is definitely our best singer; 3 I tried hard to listen but I could hardly understand anything; 4 Tom is a very good player and he usually plays well/Tom is a good player and he usually plays very well.

C: (0.5 point each) 1 make; 2 do; 3 do; 4 make; 5 make; 6 make

D: (1 point each) 1 engine; 2 show; 3 programme

E: (1 point each) 1 up; 2 turn; 3 up; 4 log

Test 5 B

A: (1 point each) 1 will feel; 2 would buy; 3 drank;
4 doesn't stop; 5 freezes; 6 had; 7 watch; 8 wouldn't
help

B: (0.5 point each) 1 Have you seen Mark recently?;
2 He will certainly write back soon; 3 I always drive
very carefully; 4 She works hard but earns hardly
any money

C: (0.5 point each) 1 do; 2 make; 3 do; 4 do; 5 make;
6 do

D: (1 point each) 1 book; 2 opera; 3 show

E: (1 point each) 1 up; 2 turn; 3 pick; 4 up

Test 6 A

A: (1 point each) 1 have hated; 2 has; 3 have lived;
4 wrote; 5 loved; 6 hasn't drunk

B: (0.5 point each) 1 was built; 2 visited; 3 had;
4 was changed; 5 is served; 6 are cleaned; 7 change;
8 offers; 9 are met; 10 are taken; 11 have stayed;
12 have been looked after

C: (0.5 point each) 1 b; 2 f; 3 c; 4 a; 5 g; 6 e

D: (1 point each) 1 floods; 2 summit; 3 avalanche;
4 foggy; 5 earthquake

Test 6 B

A: (1 point each) 1 composed; 2 have known; 3 did;
4 doesn't understand; 5 has passed; 6 moved

B: (0.5 point each) 1 have had; 2 has been; 3 served;
4 was changed; 5 offers; 6 include; 7 have been
chosen; 8 is always served; 9 never wait; 10 was;
11 was brought; 12 were given

C: (0.5 point each) 1 g; 2 f; 3 b; 4 e; 5 a; 6 c

D: (1 point each) 1 drought; 2 peaks; 3 famine;
4 drizzle; 5 glacier

Test 7 A

A: (1 point each) 1 leaves; 2 are getting; 3 return;
4 is not doing; 5 will answer; 6 leave; 7 will help;
8 is not going to give

B (1 point each) 1 does he; 2 didn't you; 3 will she;
4 have they; 5 can't you

C: (1 point each) 1 brilliant; 2 violin; 3 poor;
4 disappointing

D: (0.5 point each) 1 across; I found this dress by
chance ...; 2 set; ...decide to organise/start/establish
their own companies; 3 up; John has started judo/to
practise judo regularly ...

Test 7 B

A: (1 point each) 1 am going to learn; 2 finds; 3 will
clean; 4 is flying; 5 pass; 6 arrives; 7 come; 8 are
not doing

B: (1 point each) 1 hasn't he; 2 is it; 3 won't you;
4 didn't they; 5 do you

C: (1 point each) 1 floors; 2 disc-jockey; 3 design;
4 distorted

D: (0.5 point each) 1 out; She might feel that we forgot
about her ...; 2 miss; I would hate to lose the
opportunity to see the opening ceremony; 3 off; He
began his career as ...

Test 8 A

A: (0.5 point each) 1 whose; 2 where; 3 who; 4 X;
5 which; 6 that/which

B: (0.5 point each) 1 at; 2 on; 3 near; 4 at; 5 in; 6 on;
7 during; 8 between

C: (1 point each) 1 told/ordered Chris not to drink or
eat anything; 2 Could you help me; 3 advised my
younger sister to drink a glass of water and lie down;
4 Don't let strangers into the house; 5 asked/told/
ordered me to tidy up my room

D: (0.5 point each)
Shapes: geometric, round, square;
Materials: stone, concrete, wood, brick;
Colours: dark, light, bright

E: (0.5 point each) 1 e; 2 b; 3 g; 4 d; 5 a; 6 c

Test 8 B

A: (0.5 point each) 1 who; 2 where; 3 which/that;
4 whose; 5 X; 6 who/that

B: (0.5 point each) 1 in; 2 at; 3 near; 4 across; 5 In;
6 between; 7 during; 8 on

C: (1 point each) 1 Could you lend me some money;
2 tells me to think twice before I; 3 Don't bring any
sweets for our children; 4 I advised my mother to go;
5 asked/told Tom not to use his mobile phone

D: (0.5 point each)
Kinds of buildings: castle, office block, museum;
Lines: clear, straight, strong; Photography
equipment: zoom lens, camera, flash, tripod

E: (0.5 point each) 1 a; 2 g; 3 d; 4 b; 5 e; 6 c

Mid-year Test A

A: (1 point each) 1 have been to; 2 she interviews many
people; 3 a glass of orange juice; 4 I played football!;
5 I haven't fed them yet; 6 I don't mind opening the
window; 7 I am tired of you making ...; 8 have a
shower; 9 this wonderful black cotton; 10 can't
see you

B: (1 point each) 1 don't believe; 2 broke; 3 works;
4 is going to be; 5 has left; 6 are doing; 7 were
kissing; 8 will have

C: (0.5 point each) 1 living; 2 the other; 3 music; 4 are;
5 None; 6 don't have to; 7 the tallest; 8 a lot of

D: (0.5 point each) 1 f; 2 b; 3 g; 4 a; 5 e; 6 c

E: (0.5 point each word or expression)
Housework: clear the table;
Politics: election; Types of parties: house-warming;
Money: discount + 3 more words or expressions in
each category

F: (1 point each) 1 honest; 2 bitter; 3 wise;
4 convenient; 5 calm; 6 peaceful; 7 mild

Mid-year Test B

A: (1 point each) 1 haven't spent; 2 horrible old dark
brown sweaters; 3 was walking; 4 I good at playing
chess; 5 I enjoy listening; 6 close the door;
7 The pizza smells very good; 8 Once a week she
plays .../She plays ... once a week; 9 stays at work;
10 You don't have to tell me ...

B: (1 point each) 1 hasn't eaten; 2 will study;
3 am revising; 4 hasn't heard; 5 make; 6 called;
7 is going to jump; 8 left

C: (0.5 point each) 1 have to; 2 the other; 3 watching; 4 the; 5 worse; 6 a little; 7 neither; 8 Is

D: (0.5 point each) 1 b; 2 f; 3 c; 4 g; 5 e; 6 a

E: (0.5 point each word or expression) Negative opinion adjectives: overrated; Banks: loan; Types of houses: cottage; Jobs: plumber + 3 more words or expressions in each category

F: (1 point each) 1 hard-working; 2 reliable; 3 spicy; 4 active; 5 brave; 6 tender; 7 decisive

Final Test A

A: (1 point each) 1 nicer; 2 much; 3 Reading books; 4 do; 5 asked; 6 some; 7 she was; 8 at history; 9 will like; 10 if he doesn't

B: (1 point each) 1 have lost; 2 is taking; 3 is spoken; 4 is not going to rain; 5 was given; 6 knew

C: (0.5 point each) 1 don't have to; 2 the other; 3 was; 4 the violin; 5 any; 6 whose

D: (0.5 point each) 1 at; 2 for; 3 into; 4 of; 5 to; 6 for

E: (1 point each) 1 give; 2 down; 3 send; 4 on; 5 carry

F: (0.5 point each) 1 h; 2 b; 3 k; 4 i; 5 a; 6 j; 7 f; 8 e; 9 g; 10 c

G: (0.5 point each word or expression) Weather: breeze; Feelings: pleased; Urban problems: crime; In the house: French windows + 3 more words or expressions in each category

Final Test B

A: (1 point each) 1 stay up; 2 the week; 3 who; 4 watch football matches; 5 both; 6 which/that; 7 I'm going to watch; 8 some; 9 it starts; 10 ends

B: (1 point each) 1 was offered; 2 has broken; 3 was writing; 4 haven't seen; 5 don't apologise; 6 are not accepted

C: (0.5 point each) 1 aren't; 2 mustn't; 3 the most; 4 hard; 5 the weekend; 6 much

D: (0.5 point each) 1 for; 2 from; 3 on; 4 of; 5 of; 6 about

E: (1 point each) 1 away; 2 turns; 3 up; 4 get; 5 come

F: (0.5 point each) 1 f; 2 i; 3 a; 4 g; 5 h; 6 k; 7 c; 8 j; 9 e; 10 b

G: (0.5 point each word or expression) Personality: generous; Photography: tripod; Natural disasters: famine; TV programmes: reality show + 3 more words or expressions in each category

Skills Tests
(All 1 point each)

Test 1 Listening
1 c; 2 c; 3 c; 4 b; 5 b; 6 c; 7 b; 8a

Test 2 Reading
1 T; 2 F; 3 T; 4 F; 5 F; 6 F; 7 T; 8 T

Test A Listening
1 T; 2 T; 3 F; 4 T; 5 T; 6 F

Test A Reading
1 C; 2 G; 3 D; 4 F; 5 A; 6 B

Test 3 Listening
1 T; 2 T; 3 F; 4 T; 5 T; 6 F; 7 F; 8 F

Test 4 Reading
1 F; 2 T; 3 F; 4 T; 5 F; 6 T; 7 T; 8 T

Test B Listening
1 T; 2 T; 3 F; 4 F; 5 F; 6 T

Test B Reading
1 c; 2 a; 3 c; 4 a; 5 a; 6 a

Mid-year Test Listening
1 T; 2 F; 3 F; 4 T; 5 T; 6 F

Mid-year Test Reading
1 b; 2 c; 3 c; 4 a; 5 b; 6 b

Test 5 Listening
1 F; 2 T; 3 F; 4 F; 5 T; 6 F; 7 T; 8 T

Test 6 Reading
1 E; 2 B; 3 H; 4 A; 5 D; 6 C; 7 I; 8 G

Test C Listening
1 a; 2 c; 3 b; 4 a; 5 a; 6 b

Test C Reading
1 E; 2 A; 3 F; 4 C; 5 G; 6 B

Test 7 Listening
1 b; 2 c; 3 c; 4 a; 5 b; 6 a; 7 b; 8 c

Test 8 Reading
1 T; 2 F; 3 F; 4 F; 5 T; 6 F; 7 T; 8 F

Test D Listening
1 b; 2 c; 3 b; 4 a; 5 b; 6 c

Test D Reading
1 T; 2 F; 2 T; 4 T; 5 F; 6 T

Final Test Listening
1 T; 2 F; 3 T; 4 T; 5 F; 6 F

Final Test Reading
1 T; 2 T; 3 T; 4 F; 5 F; 6 T

Pearson Education Limited
Edinburgh Gate
Harlow, Essex
CM20 2JE
England
and Associated Companies throughout the world.

www.longman.com
© Pearson Education Limited 2006

First published 2001
Second edition 2006
Fifth impression 2009

ISBN-13: 978-0-582-85421-5

Printed in Italy by Canale

Set in ITC Officina Sans 10.5pt

Produced for the publishers by AMR Design Ltd,
Hampshire, UK (www.amrdesign.com).

Acknowledgements
We are indebted to Rik Palieri for permission to
reproduce an extract from the article 'Vermont folk
singer – America's only known Polish piper' by Peter
Clark in THE WORLD OF ENGLISH.

Cover photograph: Eastbourne Pier, East Sussex,
England © Getty Images/Image Bank

Every effort has been made to trace the copyright
holders and we apologise in advance for any
unintentional omissions. We would be pleased to
insert the appropriate acknowledgement in any
subsequent edition of this publication.